Anx

MW00653468

Take Back Control of Your Life

Zaara R. Heart

from various sources. Please consult a licensed professional before attempting any techniques outlined in this book.

By reading this document, the reader agrees that under no circumstances is the author responsible for any losses, direct or indirect, that are incurred as a result of the use of the information contained within this document, including, but not limited to, errors, omissions, or inaccuracies.

Table of Contents

Introduction

Are you sick of being anxious and want to change this - permanently? Emma Stone once told the Huffington Post: "The first time I had a panic attack…I thought the house was burning down!" Rolling Stone star John Mayer explained that his panic attacks made him feel like his sanity was slipping away, whereas singer Ellie Goulding latched onto a stranger and told them she was dying (Weingus, 2015). The severity of anxiety can differ from person to person; however, you're reading this because you've noticed that something isn't quite right anymore.

Some people suffer from spontaneous anxiety combustion where they're caught off-guard. Their heart starts beating into their throat and their vision blurs as they're about to faint. They feel a sudden jolt of panic that separates them from their bodies, and they have no idea what to expect. They were laughing and talking to a friend five minutes ago when it suddenly feels like a century has passed. The world starts spinning, and they experience a full-blown panic attack from their worst nightmares.

This is what it looks like for someone who experiences anxiety that jumps out of nowhere. What they don't realize is that it's often snowballed subconsciously, and they just weren't paying attention or managing it as it came. Maybe Sam's week started with conflict at work. He avoided this and went on to meet a friend at the local hangout. His friend shared some bad news that caused Sam to worry that night, keeping him awake. Tuesday came with silly irritations where he forgot to pay his utilities, and he had to take time off work to sort it out.

Wednesday was a flurry of fatigue but it came with more challenges. Sam dodges many minor obstacles spread out over the week. They all seem tiny and manageable until Saturday strikes. More bad news creeps up on him when he gets a phone call to confirm that his good friend was admitted to the hospital after an accident. Now, his heart rate increases and there's an unexplainable battle for air. Sam experiences a panic attack because all the small irritations have led to a momentous ball of anxiety.

Other people are fortunate and don't reach this point before they seek help. Maybe Sarah has noticed that her life hasn't been what she expects it to be for a while now. She adopted new habits to avoid the minor stresses thrown her way. Sarah instead stops speaking to her partner because it leads to confrontation every time. She knows that it makes her uncomfortable, but she just can't deal with it right now. Sarah is using avoidance to deny her anxiety and this will eventually lead to Sam's example once she can't manage all the little things anymore.

The truth is that none of us want to experience anxiety. We all wish to lead lives as simple as the movies display. Unfortunately, the symptoms of anxiety can range anywhere between mild headaches and agitation to periods that make us think our life is about to end. Severe anxiety is an ironic situation. It happens when our fears are ignited by events or people, but the revolving fear returns when we are frightened of what the future holds. Fear is both the cause and effect of anxiety.

Anxiety is nothing to be ashamed of and you certainly don't need to avoid it. Everyone experiences fear in their life, no matter where it comes from. Anxiety is the most common emotional disorder in the US and affects about 40 million people according to the Anxiety and Depression Association of America or ADAA (ADAA, n.d.-b). That makes 18% of Americans anxious annually. Even worse, is the fact that anxiety is perfectly treatable but only 36% of people learn to manage it. The problem doesn't only lie in America. One in every 13 people globally has anxiety at any given time.

Not recognizing anxiety or choosing not to manage it can be detrimental to you. How often have you felt like something in your life is holding you back from your full potential? You know that you're not alone now and the only way to improve the quality of your life is by learning how to deal with life and all its glorious unpredictability. It doesn't matter what anxiety you experience. You might panic in social settings, or you might overthink everything and delay opportunities. Maybe you're afraid of striving for your goals because you can't speak in public.

Anxiety might carry many faces, but it doesn't change the fact that managing it *is* possible. Ask yourself a few questions.

Do you want more from life?

Would you like to face fears that control you?

Are you willing to do what is within your capacity to alleviate worries?

Do you want to have a collection of anxiety management tools that could open doors you never imagined?

I've been in your shoes that are filled with uncertainty, unfamiliarity, and anxiety. It took me time to master my emotions and reduce the effects of this debilitating crutch. I managed to control my anxiety and redirect my life as I wanted it to flow. No one but me is allowed to drive my train. It was a fulfilling journey with many ups and downs, but I managed to win and wear my anxiety like a war medal. I took my passion and desire to erase anxiety to the next level and started helping other people reach my point. Too many people know the painful experience anxiety brings.

It isn't always a physical pain either because we feel deprived of a life we deserve. It wasn't long before my guidance burst into a support group. The best person to help anyone is someone who's experienced the loss and setbacks from anxiety. I offered support and taught the group how to deal with the common enemy. Anxiety matters deeply to me and my goal is to help you next. My experience, knowledge, and passion have helped many before you, and it will give you a foundation that can't be shattered by anxiety again.

You'll learn how anxiety develops, including all the factors that contribute to it. Various types can disrupt your life and it doesn't help to only have a general understanding. Anxiety can't be described as one feeling or experience. It relates to various problems that could be setting you back. There are some symptoms you might be well aware of, and then there are those that seem like the most normal thing on earth. You'll understand where they originate from and figure out your personal triggers.

Just as anxiety has many definitions, so do you have a multitude of reasons for feeling the way you do. Triggers are hiding in plain sight and don't need to be frightening when you learn how to manage them. The good news is that we have more reasons to prevent anxiety than we do to avoid it. The physiological impact can be minor or severe, depending on how long you've been exposed to it. The feeling of losing your mind isn't as weird as it seems either.

Anxiety isn't defined by people who talk to invisible friends, but the consequences can make you think that you'll lose your mind. It's all about finding the unique triggers that relate to you so that you can build a management default that works. Multiple clinical studies have proven the efficiency of what I'm about to teach you (Hofmann et al., 2010). I didn't rely on anything but proven methods to defeat anxiety and I don't expect you to do this either.

Some techniques are so simple that you can practice them daily for 10 minutes. Other methods take longer, but they are enjoyable as a bonus. When was the last time you truly enjoyed something? Mild anxiety can be managed with instant relievers and severe anxiety can be targeted with strategies that you design time-wise. I've left no stone unturned and I've included breathing techniques that prevent you from experiencing genuine physical consequences.

Too many books include the art of controlled breathing, but they skip the real threat of improper deep breathing. Learning to breathe incorrectly can have dire side effects. Moreover, I'll teach you the finer art of relaxing your body and mind with proven techniques. Once more, it's easy to tell someone to relax, but there's a science behind it. I provide the steps you need to ensure that calming down in a time of need is but a few seconds away.

This book includes ancient practices that help you self-manage your anxiety, but it also provides medical and psychological advice. Your entire life will become new with small and easily manageable changes that even the most anxious at heart can implement. You won't only learn about the changes you can subtly use; you'll also learn why you need to do it. Not everything is common sense and some deeper research, trial, and error are required to learn what genuinely works.

There's no kind of anxiety, no depth you've fallen into, or consequences you can't return from. Life hasn't stopped when anxiety chose you. Every technique, support method, and medical recommendation is here for you. It's all at your fingertips now. Welcome to the journey that starts when you continue reading or listening to this guide.

Chapter 1:

Understanding Anxiety:

Causes, Symptoms, and

Variations

Anxiety means something different to everyone, as some experience healthy levels and other people experience a fear that can't be described. Unfortunately, many people don't know the true meaning of anxiety and what its purpose is in our lives. That's why you'll learn about the fundamentals, common symptoms, and understand the various kinds, both good and bad. It's hard to think that anxiety can be a good thing, but you'll realize why I say this.

Comprehensive Perceptions

For some, the thought of anxiety brings about a deeper fear. For others, they might only know the good side of it and would like to get it under control with proper self-management now. Know this, anxiety can be the master, or you can control it. There's no need to become enslaved to it because you'll stand tall with some gentle, caring, and understanding guidance from someone who's been there and done that, irrespective of how bad you suffer from the dreaded emotion. The word 'emotion' plays a key role in understanding what anxiety is because it's described as both a good and bad emotion.

It's simply another word for fear, worry, dread, unease, nervousness, and a perceived threat to your well-being or life. Having a healthy amount of fear is the same as being nervous about a job interview, moving to a new home, or starting life after college. Anxiety is experienced by everyone on some level at any given time during their life. The person who stays home because of social fears has anxiety. Someone who avoids enclosed spaces is afraid of being unable to escape. Many people have a fear of public speaking, even if they aren't aware of it because they haven't been in a situation that called for it.

Mild anxiety is simply the body's reaction to a perceived threat and is perfectly normal. Ancient humans didn't have all the comforts and safety we have today. They relied on survival instincts to eat, sleep, and socialize. Cavemen weren't the top of the food chain, but they needed to survive. Our brains have evolved this primal instinct to preserve our bodies and minds. Threats are perceived as danger and this starts an automatic response in our biological being. Your body enters this state multiple times daily without you realizing it. What happens when you slam the brakes because the driver in front of you has abruptly stopped?

How can you explain the time you jumped out of the road just in time to miss the car that was speeding towards you? Your reaction towards the imminent danger has protected you by stirring the fight, flight, or freeze response. This response even happens when you get called into your employer's office and don't know what to expect. Your heart rate increases and your palms become sweaty. You feel nervous even though you don't have a valid reason to be anxious, but even good anxiety is part of the preservation of our being and helps us prepare for what's to come.

Unfortunately, this can snowball into bigger problems when we deny the accumulation of our fears. It doesn't matter if they're good or bad. Compare your fears to a suitcase you must pack before flying to your vacation destination. The airline only allows so much weight and this is how the anxiety response works in our brains. Every tiny fear is packed into the suitcase if it's not handled. This includes the nervousness you feel about meeting someone new, speaking up about displeasures at home, or the stressful route you always seem to encounter on your way to work. Eventually, these subconscious fears have used all the weight allowances in the suitcase and it can't close anymore.

Dealing with your anxiety is like rearranging the suitcase and removing fears that don't belong there. Someone who denies their fears or unknowingly ignores them is over packing this suitcase until it pops open. Severe and prolonged anxiety is overwhelming. This is when we finally cross the line between normal nervousness and fear that disrupts our daily lives. The fight, flight, or freeze response can manifest itself in physical, mental, and emotional reactions you've never experienced before. The accumulation of dangers poses too much threat to our well-being and the brain retaliates.

So, it doesn't only take a life-changing threat to cause severe anxiety. It can also happen when you allow the small fears to add up to an enormous monster that makes your life difficult. The emotional part of the brain called the amygdala signals the hypothalamus gland to preserve you at all costs. This little gland sends instructions to the adrenal glands near your kidneys and adrenaline and cortisol flood through your veins. It's a biological reaction to protect you.

For example, the less common freeze mode is entered when your primal reaction is to be invisible to the predatorial threat. This happens when you can't move and your voice has lost its volume. It's most commonly experienced in trauma. Your muscles become tense and you can't do what needs to be done to avoid the threat.

The flight mode is when your body reacts by running away from the danger. Your blood pressure increases when the adrenaline reaches your heart and causes a faster pace. This is the body's way of stimulating the muscles and readying you for the escape. You experience this when you're walking alone, see a threatening group headed your way, and quickly turn around. Adrenaline is a good chemical, but only if it's ignited by real threats and used to protect you.

The fight mode is similar to the previous reaction, except that it floods your body with adrenaline in preparation for defense. You might feel muscle tension increase again as the body prepares them for usage.

Your muscles are used to run or fight because strength isn't found in relaxed muscles. That's why the body tenses up, even though it's counterintuitive to wrongly perceived threats. You'll become defensive when facing fears, such as natural disasters, accidents, or preparing for a work presentation.

Your eyesight, breathing, pain perception, and even your blood changes. Our blood prepares to clot up when we perceive a threat because clotting is needed to help you when you're injured. Your fight, flight, or freeze mode is a natural reaction and it differs from person to person and situation to situation. You might use flight mode for one incident and freeze mode for another. The truth is that you'll never know how you'll react until you face fear.

Once these responses happen daily and your feelings of anxiety are persistently strong, it can interfere with daily tasks, keep you from leaving your house, and make you enjoy previously loved activities less. It can also interfere with your work performance and prevent social interactions which are more important than you think. You'll know why socializing is a keystone of this hindrance soon. Anyone who suffers from prolonged and persistent anxiety for six months or more or experiences fear that interrupts their life might have an anxiety disorder.

It's not a matter of whether the chicken or egg came first then. All that matters is that you learn more about it and start unpacking the overloaded suitcase before it pops. Anyone, including you, can change your anxiety.

Types of Anxiety

Anxiety is the most common form of emotional turmoil that affects every age group and is most common in women (Holland, 2018). There's no shame in being anxious, but it can take an amazing life away from you when you walk around with constant, unexplainable fear. Seven major types other than general anxiety disorder (GAD) can impact anyone.

Panic disorder is rather debilitating. It happens when you experience recurrent and sometimes unexplainable panic attacks. It's an abrupt feeling of utter panic or fear that starts in minutes. The intensity can even feel like you're having a heart attack and most sufferers fear having another one after they've experienced it. Often, the overwhelming terror that stirs is triggered by something that isn't dangerous, but that doesn't stop the physical symptoms from wreaking havoc. You can feel as though the world is about to end for no apparent reason. The symptoms alone can make you panic further when your heart is racing and you can't breathe; however, the disorder is perfectly treatable and manageable.

Social anxiety disorder (SAD) is another common contender. Some people even call it social phobia because it's a genuine fear when you walk into a room filled with people and start panicking. The level of fear is indescribable to someone who hasn't experienced it. People with social anxiety disorder might struggle to socialize, speak to other people, or meet new friends. It's not shyness because it actually interferes with your social life. It can manifest its nasty head at school, work, and even at home. You might also feel nervous about upcoming social events that aren't even set in stone yet, but this type only prevents you from having the support you need.

Obsessive-compulsive disorder (OCD) is often misunderstood. It's also chronic anxiety that disrupts your life. It presents itself in obsessions that lead to compulsive behavior, even unintentional ones. Take someone with a lucky pair of socks. They feel insecure if they aren't wearing them. Someone who checks a door lock three times is also afraid and needs to act compulsively to ensure that their fear subsides a little. This disorder is a collection of rituals that you may develop to feel safer in your environment. Unfortunately, these repetitive thoughts awaken behavior that could manifest in ways even you don't want to behave. Obsessions are your perceived thoughts about a situation and compulsiveness is the urge you feel to repeat your ritualistic behavior.

Phobias are also anxiety disorders, in which you can feel an irrational fear of something non-threatening. It can be a fear of elevators, spiders, or staircases. The only difference between GAD and phobias is that the latter is a specified fear of an object, place, or even person. You can have more than one phobia too. The effects of phobias can range from mild to severely debilitating. A mild phobia is seen in claustrophobic people who don't like enclosed spaces but will make exceptions; however, a severe phobia is seen when someone's teeth rot because their fear of dentists is beyond negotiations. Phobias are real but that doesn't mean it can't be treated because the only way to overcome fear is by facing it.

Post-traumatic stress disorder (PTSD) might be the worst anxiety disorder that exists, but the good news is that it's also fixable. It's often experienced by people who've seen nightmarish things. This includes military veterans, natural disaster survivors, and those who recover from a traumatic accident. Sexual assault, abuse, and terrible childhoods could also cause this disorder. These people feel a heightened sense of danger because their fight, flight, or freeze modes have fallen off the edge. They can perceive danger when none exists.

For example, a wine cork pops and the person's brain goes into the protective reaction when it connects this trigger with the sound of gunshots in Vietnam. Know this, having PTSD doesn't make you weak or any less of a person. It develops after such traumatic events took place that your brain restructured your preservation response. We were only built to see and experience so much, anything beyond this would cause an imbalance of the brain's reactions. However, it can be undone, just like any other anxiety disorder.

Separation anxiety disorder is another common problem. Many of us think about early childhood development when our kids experience separation anxiety, but little do most people know that it affects adults too. It usually develops in childhood or is adopted through genetics, but it can also be erased. People with disorder have this deep fear of being separated from their loved ones. They can't fathom being alone or without the person that they've attached themselves to.

Relationships, whether it's between parents and children or between partners, must be healthy and allow each party some freedom. Separation anxiety can change this because relationships aren't healthy when you can't separate from the other person. You must have your freedom at some point, and so must they. This disorder commonly affects divorced people or someone who lost another to death, and it can impact your life after a big move.

Health anxiety is the final disorder you need to learn about. It's also called hypochondria and doubles as a phobia. It's defined as an unrealistic fear of having a serious medical condition without there being any evidence of it. Some people even go to doctors to find out that nothing's wrong, and they end up with a prescription for anxiety medication. The truth is that your imagination is one of the most powerful parts of your brain, and imagined symptoms can seem very real. Even a minor ache can be misconstrued for a life-threatening condition. The reason this disorder is counterproductive is that anxiety makes you feel sick, such as the panic attacks that feel like heart attacks. Don't worry though because it's another treatable condition.

Identifying Symptoms

Anxiety has a horrible way of manifesting itself. Some symptoms are subtle but others can make a hypochondriac have a real panic attack. You might feel a loss of control between your mind and body when butterflies swarm your stomach and you become dizzy. Some people even suffer from nightmares because their subconscious minds are projecting images of their fears. The rumination of painful thoughts and memories are also symptoms, and so is the general discomfort you unexpectedly feel when you walk into a room.

Feeling restless, fearful, anxious, and dread for no apparent reason are signs that you might need an intervention. Anxiety even clouds your concentration and you struggle to focus on the task at hand. It can prevent you from falling asleep at night. Your breathing becomes shallow and rapid as your heart sprints. The hyperventilation causes your heart to pump faster because it isn't getting enough oxygen. You might start sweating, trembling, twitching, or become lethargic and weak. You'll feel an urge to avoid your fear and obsessions might sink into your thoughts.

Your digestive system can also go haywire when you suffer from diarrhea, nausea, or nervous vomiting. You could lose your appetite or find comfort in food. Maybe you find yourself ruminating on past events that were most traumatic? All of these symptoms can trigger an anxiety attack.

Anxiety Attack Symptoms

Anxiety attacks often involve at least four worrisome symptoms that could make you think you're about to implode. Shortness of breath, heart palpitations, extreme sweating, tremors, and the sensation that you're choking or smothering are common. Other symptoms are pain or tightness in your chest, nausea, dizziness, fainting, sudden body temperature fluctuations, dry mouth, and numbness or tingling. You might experience depersonalization where you don't feel like yourself anymore. The fear of dying or losing your sanity could also creep in. The symptoms can feel real and may send you to the emergency room often. Anxiety attacks mimic genuine life-threatening conditions for some people. You'll be experiencing panic attacks as part of panic disorder, but anxiety attacks can hit anyone at any time.

Where it Originates

Researchers haven't been able to pinpoint the precise origin of our anxiety, but they concur that it's instigated by various factors (Felman & Browne, 2020).

Environmental stressors are one contributor, and it includes your work, financial, home, family, and romantic life if you have difficulty in any of them.

Genetics also works against us because you're more likely to become anxious if it runs in your family.

Medical factors can also turn you into an anxious person. You might be fearing surgery or have experienced a prolonged recovery from one. The stress that causes anxiety can also come from other diseases and their symptoms. It might arise from medications as well.

Brain chemistry is certainly another contributor because it impacts your hormone levels and electrical activity in the brain.

Trauma is known to be a cause for anxiety. It's a cause, trigger, and magnifier, especially if you have a high-strung personality and are sensitive to challenges. Our personality traits are also genetic and being sensitive is a trait. A genome study was conducted to confirm whether twins with the anxiety sensitive (AS) gene that designs their personality were experiencing more anxiety than their siblings (Davies et al., 2015). Twins who had the AS gene present were struggling to live their best lives compared to their siblings who were absent of the gene and leading happier lives. Sensitivity lies within our genes and personalities, but we can build resilience towards it with proper management. That's what this book is for.

Finally, the withdrawals experienced from illicit substances can also send recovering addicts into anxiety. Withdrawal symptoms intensify the effects of fear and dread.

Psychological problems like depression and addiction can cause such amplification of your anxiety if you're only treating the symptoms and neglecting the source that your fears become untreatable. You must focus on the sources and erase them first. This doesn't mean that there's anything wrong with you that can't be fixed. The good news is that we don't live in the dark ages anymore and there are so many options for you to diminish any potential underlying issues causing more anxiety.

Many people have specific triggers that make matters worse. Identifying them will help you overcome your fears and live the life you deserve. We're going to focus on triggers in Chapter Three. However, let's see what you can avoid when you manage your anxiety first.

Chapter 2:

The Physiological and Psychological Effects of Anxiety

Anxiety can have serious long-term consequences, and the risk only increases with prolonged or chronic experiences. We can't escape the possibilities, but we can reshape them by preventing them from happening in the first place. Use the information here to design a journey forward where you can prevent these needless problems, or use the knowledge to improve your overall well-being if you've experienced some setbacks already. No hole you can ever fall in is deep enough to be inescapable. You deserve everything you desire and that includes a life free from the anxiety crutch, especially because some risks are so severe.

What You Want to Avoid Physically

Most of us will experience what feels like shallow breathing, increased heart rates, and a migraine that lingers endlessly after feeling stressed. These are only some of the symptoms you could experience if you refuse to manage your anxiety properly. You've learned about what happens when your brain retaliates into a preservation mode, which we'll simply call the stress response now. Yes, this response is great when you're faced with a bear in the wild. Bears are genuine threats, but is this response doing you any good as you hyperventilate before a presentation at work?

Your heart speeds up and you're pouring bucket loads of sweat that seeps through your crisp, white shirt you chose for the meeting. If you enter such a severely anxious reaction to a situation that isn't equally threatening, you might very well be experiencing abnormal anxiety which may be happening after chronic levels of stress have told your brain to cancel the return flight from this response. Now, you've become edgy, easily startled, and this looming sense of doom follows you everywhere. Whether you're working on managing the response to lead a happier life and avoid consequences, or if you're worried about how it has already impacted your body, you must learn more.

Addressing severe or prolonged anxiety isn't only about improving the quality of your life, but it's also a method of avoiding serious health complications that are possible for anyone who suffers from it. The stress response happens to protect us from genuine or unrealistic threats, and it also activates the brain's heightened processes so that you can deal with the problem you face. Think about it as awakening the brain. This is a physical response because the brain controls every inch of your body. Unfortunately, this response can also be too intense and lead to immediate physical discomfort when you feel nausea or become lightheaded.

The more often you experience the flood of stress hormones, the more likely you become to experience it again. The frequency of your symptoms can multiply and those glands we spoke about can forget how to switch this protective reaction off. Your central nervous system (CNS) becomes used to a new normal. And even though your symptoms can decrease until the next attack, you still have excess hormones in your blood that cause problems across your body. Anxiety isn't only a psychological problem because it has physical manifestations that start with the brain.

Would you believe that the brain and gut are connected? Digestive problems are common with anxiety like nausea or lost appetites. Your appetite can also increase, putting you at greater risk for unhealthy weight gain if that's something you want to avoid. The cortisol hormone blocks nonessential functions in your body while you're in the stress response. Your digestion is blocked and the stomach muscles are relaxed by adrenaline. Harvard Medical School has confirmed that the digestive tract is under attack and irritable bowel syndrome coincides with anxiety (Harvard Health Publishing, 2010).

They also found a strong connection between anxiety and heart disease. Anxiety and panic attacks create a rapid pulse, palpitations, fluttering, and chest pain. The heart plays a role in the stress response because it increases your rhythm to ensure that enough blood reaches the regions of the brain responsible for the preservation and cognitive processes. The cardiovascular system, including the heart and your blood pressure, can't cope if they function continuously at this rate. High blood pressure can result in heart failure or stroke. You're at risk for these severe complications if you don't manage your anxiety as your suitcase fills up. You want the brain to switch back to normal mode.

A condition called vasoconstriction also occurs when your cardiovascular system is working overtime. This means that your heart is pumping blood faster to every muscle in your body and ensuring that they receive additional nutrients and oxygen to defend you. Unfortunately, this condition is better understood as a narrowing of your arteries. Your body temperature increases during this narrowing process and can lead to hot flashes. The human body is capable of compensating for imbalances like this and will work on cooling your system down again. The bad news is that it learns to overcompensate when you're chronically anxious and it plunges your body temperature, causing chills.

It's common knowledge that a fever is a sign of the body fighting an infection. However, the only time a body must fluctuate its temperature is to eradicate infections. Your temperature can also change during sleep cycles because energy must be restored to your muscular system. These changes are meant to be temporary and not long-term. It's like running a car until the heat gauge hits the red and then spraying it down with ice-cold water immediately before considering the consequences of a sudden temperature change. You could crack your radiator if you do this to a car. So, what do you think it does to the human body? Another example would be purposely giving someone hypothermia which is a sudden and unsustainable drop in body temperature when they're burning with fever.

Remaining in a heightened state of alertness is weakening your immune system too. Brief spurts of stress are good for the immune system, but prolonged cortisol can prevent your body from releasing inflammatory chemicals when you get sick. Colds, influenza, and many other viral infections are automatically targeted by inflammatory hormones. Think about someone who gets coronavirus. Their bodies cause inflammation around the lungs to keep it protected and fight the infection. Remove this inflammatory response and the person is at risk for complications. A weakened immune system can make you more susceptible to serious or irritating viral infections.

Your respiratory system is also under stress when you're anxious or experience a panic attack. Some people only ever experience one anxiety attack in their lives, but chronic sufferers can experience them often enough to become familiar with everyone in the emergency room. Anxiety causes a short and rapid breath, which is known as hyperventilation. The problem is that your breathing isn't reaching deep enough and your body and brain become deprived of higher oxygen levels. That's why you become dizzy, lightheaded, or nauseous. People with chronic obstructive pulmonary disease (COPD) or asthma can spend a lot of time in the hospital thanks to anxiety.

Their breathing is already compromised and oxygen isn't recycling as it should. They experience thoracic breathing, whereas diaphragmatic breathing is required. The latter kind is where you take a deep breath and the air passes into your stomach or diaphragm, passing all the major organs. Thoracic breathing means that the air isn't passing the chest area because you're breathing too fast. So, your body really is struggling for breath when you need that brown paper bag. Prolonged experiences like this can cause damage to the organs that need oxygen to function properly. You might even feel tingling or weakness when oxygen stops reaching your brain. We'll focus on this more in Chapter Five.

Other problems can arise when you suffer from unexplainable migraines, muscle tension, and insomnia. Insomnia just makes matters worse because you become more anxious when you aren't getting the restorative sleep your brain and body need. Your brain is working while you sleep to repair any damages in your body. Losing sleep will only make you feel worse.

Another physical manifestation of anxiety is an odd one to understand. It's often blamed on evolutionary reasons because having an empty bladder makes an escape easier. Some people experience an increased urge to urinate when they're anxious. A loss of urinary control is also one of the less popular truths, especially for people with specific phobias. This is commonly seen in movies where a child is so frightened that they wet themselves. It can happen to adults too. It's simply part of the startle response that's compromised when people feel nervous.

You need to understand that it all starts in the brain and that's why psychological damage interferes with physical functions in the body.

Psychological Consequences

Chronic anxiety can lead to a compromised CNS that starts showing psychological problems. Please note that I'm not calling anxious people who become depressed some form of crazy. I also suffered from it, so I'd have to call myself derogatory names. The brain is a complicated system and unless a psychiatrist diagnoses you with schizophrenia or psychotic disorder, you're not mentally ill. People are so afraid of mental ailments, but everyone probably experiences it at least once during their lifetime. This could be depression or anxiety as well. It isn't psychotic in nature, so don't allow stigmas to hold you back from improving your mental state. Yes, you can and will improve your mental acuity and wellness by managing your anxiety.

I'm going to help you understand how anxiety affects your mental well-being and places you at risk for setbacks in life. The Journal of Frontiers in Neuroscience has published some incredible evidence that shows us what happens in the brain under anxious responses (Robinson et al., 2013). The research on the effects of anxiety on our cognitive processes is necessary because it comes at a high cost to people. The word cognition translates directly to the processing of information. It's how your brain conceptualizes, recognizes, and translates stimuli before making a decision. Many factors are involved in processing. A thought ignites once you see, hear, smell, taste, or feel something.

Thoughts are processed according to stored memories so that you decide how to react. Your emotions interrupt the process between a memory and a thought. Emotional processing is called hot cognition and neutral processing is called cold cognition. If we bring anxiety into the equation, we have two kinds as well. Adaptive anxiety is how your brain processes a genuine threat, such as facing a bear in the woods. Maladaptive anxiety is when your brain incorrectly processes a work presentation as danger when it needn't be. That lays the groundwork of how your cognitive processes work and how it can either be adaptive or realistic, or it can be maladaptive or unrealistic.

Maladaptive cognition happens when you suffer prolonged or chronic anxiety. Remember that the brain forgets how to switch back to the adaptive state if it learns that you're best protected if it remains in the state of full alertness. The first part of cognitive processing is called the sensory-perceptual processes. This is when your senses trigger the brain for the earliest processing. The second type is called attention or control cognition. This determines whether you can stay focused on a task while processing the information in front of you. The third one is called memory cognition which is the maintenance and retrieval process. The fourth one is called executive function, and this is the part where you decide on the reaction you'll take.

Every situation you face is run through each of the four cognitions to create an outcome. People with chronic anxiety tend to run hot cognitions where the emotional part of the brain is more likely to influence the processing steps. Now you understand how PTSD sufferers are easily startled when they hear sounds that remind them of gunshots. The memory cognition becomes tainted with emotional influence and their startle response is highly activated. Someone with hot cognitions can also become shell-shocked when they reach the attention cognition because their fear of the spider is so incredible that they lose all focus. Simply, this is also how the freeze mode works when people are frozen with fear.

The Journal published a study that wanted to confirm the interruptions in each process. For eons, anxiety experiments were conducted on animals, but humans are unique. So, they proposed anticipated shock therapy while participants had to complete increasingly difficult tasks. Some tasks would bring an unpredictable shock and others would be safe. Participants were warned about the impending shocks before each task, but not when it would happen. They were also placed in unfamiliar environments to increase their anxiety further. All the conditions were controlled and the research was necessary.

Let's say that your goal is to finish the task. This means that your working memory, or the cognition process for it, must distinguish and retrieve knowledge you already know. Maybe it's a math problem and you must use a formula learned in school. The test subjects who anticipated electrical shocks before completing a task were showing problems in this process. In fact, their results were proving as complicated as the control group who suffered from chronic anxiety. Emotions rose which also interrupted the attention cognition, and their executive processing was strained. Simply, they weren't performing under anxiety, whether it was induced or not. Memory, focus, and problem-solving are damaged under the stress response.

Translate this evidence to yourself if you suffer from chronic anxiety and your brain refuses to exit this reaction. It can have a domino effect that runs through your psychological well-being when you can't finish a project at college. Once your brain slips into undcsirable processing, you can become depressed. Depression is easily ignited by feeling disappointed or worthless. Someone who can't hand their project in on time feels like they let the entire world down. Our cognitive processes are responsible for keeping us away from emotional turmoil, but we can become depressed when we use emotional reasoning or hot cognitions alone. Our emotions are powerful, and they can interfere with all four processes, turning your anxiety into a maladaptive version.

Depression is a pit that consumes your happiness, and those thoughts of being worthless are anything but reliable. The disruption of your executive function can make you feel like you can't do anything right. You start struggling to cope with regular, daily tasks and responsibilities. Many people try to find coping mechanisms that can reduce the feelings of depression. They turn to alcohol, narcotics, and even prescription medication. You might not even know that you're depressed until your partner asks you why you have no libido anymore. Depression can also decrease your sex drive. You might even experience pain in a different light because your processing can't determine how intense it is.

This is how people become withdrawn and isolate themselves. They don't know how to cope with or process regular information and everything becomes insurmountable to them. They give up because why must they continue trying when they don't have what it takes? This downward trajectory is frightening, but it's possible and not too complicated to change it. You might've experienced some of the consequences and found yourself spiraling, and you don't want a life that contains setbacks. The fact that you're reading this book tells me that you may be concerned about your future, even if you've only experienced the mildest of symptoms and consequences.

Ask yourself whether you're worried about the potential problems to come? If so, you have everything you need to prevent them. Being aware of the risks to your health isn't something you'd want to dive into, but it lays the groundwork for finding the motivation to change it. I advise that you seek some additional care if you feel like you aren't coping with the underlying problems like depression. Managing your anxiety without dealing with your depression is like expecting the sun to rise in the west. You're going to learn about many amazing coping strategies and management tools in the coming chapters, but depression mustn't be ignored.

Let's move on to find out what triggers anxiety so that you can get to the good part.

Chapter 3:

How to Identify Your

Triggers

Triggers, and I don't necessarily mean the kind you find on guns, is the first place you look to start managing your anxiety. They differ from person to person and identifying them is a practical notch on the journey to being less anxious. Some can be avoided and others can be faced like when someone gets back on the horse. Our fears only have the power we allow them to possess. You can face your triggers even if it seems impossible. And if all else fails, you can learn to manage them so that they don't harm you anymore.

Defining Triggers

Although anxiety can feel like something that popped up overnight, with time, many people will learn to recognize the triggers that cause it. Triggers are situations, experiences, sounds, sights, words, and even photos that can turn your stomach with dread and fear. It can be identified as anything that makes you feel

33

uneasy or fearful. It can be a person, a place, and with PTSD, a memory. It can be something you consume or expected financial troubles. It's important to know that triggers are not the cause of anxiety. They only cue the response in your brain. Causes are the genetic factors and lack of coping skills you learned about.

Triggers don't cause your anxiety, but they exacerbate the feelings of fear you experience. Think of the trigger as the cue that starts the first cognitive process which ultimately leads to the stress response. The fact that they differ between you and another person is the reason why you must identify them. Stressful or perceivably threatening experiences, feelings, and events are what trigger your anxiety to change from the dormant emotion lying in the amygdala to the erratic reaction agoraphobic people have when they get stuck in an elevator. The triggers help pile the suitcase to a bursting point when they accumulate.

You might be one of many people who have multiple triggers, and this only means that you need to manage them speedily. The second issue is that some triggers naturally lead to anxiety. You may not even see them as triggers and could dismiss them from your recognition. For example, being asked to present the latest product to a room full of people at work is a natural trigger for anyone with performance anxiety. You might not consider it a stressful situation but it is if it worries you. Your anxiety suitcase starts filling up because you aren't acknowledging the natural triggers. High-stress situations, chronic illness, and unhealthy relationships are going to lead to anxiety.

These triggers might feel like regular life to other people, but you can feel a knot in your stomach when you think about being ill for the remainder of your life. You might not even feel the snowballing discomfort growing inside of you when your partner constantly undermines you or makes snarky comments about how you've gained a few pounds. These triggers can't be forgotten even if it seems like everyone deals with the same problems, so why must you complain? Different people have varying tolerance for anxiety, and just because something doesn't trigger another person, it doesn't mean that it won't affect you.

It's time for you to learn about triggers, natural or not, so that you can manage them and reduce your anxiety intensity.

Triggers Galore!

Some triggers will surprise you and others will make you realize that there's nothing natural about them. Many of them are experienced by people you know, but some of them can tolerate certain cues better than you. You'll have strengths that work better than theirs too. Your anxiety might be triggered by memories and a friend might have problems with a consumable trigger. Let's learn about them so that you can choose to avoid or manage each.

The fear of social interactions might not seem obvious to some people. Attending a friend's party, performing actions in front of other people, and speaking to new people are triggers that make you feel uncomfortable. However, you can't avoid these triggers in your daily life. You can't avoid your boss, partner, friends, or lecturers. Interacting with other people is a necessity of life, whether we're comfortable or not. You need to recognize whether these interactions are causing you unease though because then you can manage them. Don't try to be like your social butterfly friend if you become anxious interacting with new people without managing it correctly.

Even performance anxiety is seemingly natural because who doesn't fear a crowd of spectators judging them? Well, some people are rather comfortable with this. Being afraid of public speaking doesn't guarantee that you'll never need to present an idea in front of 20 colleagues, though. You might also not be able to avoid giving a toast at someone's wedding if they're depending on you. Anticipating and planning for these situations, expected or unpredictable, is how you deal with your emotions before you give your toast. Bringing a friend along to a new group activity can also help you find comfort, but sadly, we can't avoid performing in front of a group every time. If it can't be avoided, then it must be managed. There are ways to get around it because not everyone has performance anxiety even if it seems that way.

Medications are also another natural trigger because most people don't read the side effects. For example, Bevispas is an over-the-counter (OTC) medication that does wonders for IBS. However, take a moment to read the insert. It warns you that it can trigger anxiety and depression. Some medications and supplements are making you anxious. You could be setting your chemical balance off unintentionally. Talk to your doctor and weigh the pros and cons. Birth control pills, weight loss supplements, cold medicine, and decongestants also contain trigger ingredients.

Food and water aren't something you'd consider, but it can trigger anxiety as well. Dehydration can cause hormonal imbalances that make you anxious. Some people are sensitive to the food dyes and artificial sweeteners that our processed food contains so much of today (Owens, n.d.) Other ingredients can also cause harm and you'll learn about them later. For now, know that the food and drinks you consume are responsible for the balance in your body. Never skip a meal either because that's an easily avoidable trigger that pushes your chemical balance out of the window. Skipping meals and becoming dehydrated is a sure-fire method of becoming anxious.

The National Library of Medicine also published an article confirming that caffeine is another consumable trigger (Lara, 2010). The study found that people with existing anxiety are especially sensitive to the exacerbating effects of caffeine. Coffee isn't the only source of it either. Most sodas also contain caffeine. So does chocolate, some ice-cream, certain weight loss medications, pain relievers, energy drinks, and alcohol. Drugs, nicotine, and alcohol are consumable triggers on their own. You need to start choosing what you consume more carefully because this trigger can be prevented even if it's not experienced by everyone.

Sleep disturbances are another trigger. You must avoid the effects of sleeplessness. You know that the brain restores the body during your sleep cycles and any disruptions will lead to greater anxiety. Sometimes, we don't realize how it affects us until we remove the cause of sleeplessness. Blue light from screens can instruct the brain to falsely believe that it's daytime and keeps you awake. The environment can also be controlled by you. Make sure the room temperature is suitable for sleeping. Block as much natural light out as you can too. We'll deal with sleeplessness in Chapter Nine.

Your health is one of the biggest natural triggers when you're diagnosed with cancer or any chronic condition that changes the quality or longevity of your life. The best way to handle the fear that comes from the unknown is to learn how to manage it. Everyone experiences this anxiety when they get diagnosed with life-changing conditions. You can't change your diagnosis, but you can take steps to lead a healthier life if you have diabetes for example. Be proactive when discussing your options with a doctor and listen to the recommendations you must follow to keep yourself at the peak of possibility.

Negative thinking is another common natural trigger that most of us don't even realize. Your cognitive processing might be controlling the way you feel, but it can also be influenced by your thoughts, perceptions, and self-talk. Do yourself a favor and tell a friend that they look pale and sick. Ask them what's wrong or if they feel unwell. Watch as they start speaking negativity over themselves and you might even see their complexion change. It's a cruel experiment but the power of our words is greater than you think because the brain listens and responds. Most of the negative thoughts you possess are of yourself. Become conscious of your spoken language and inner voice to gradually reduce this trigger.

Conflict is a trigger that seems natural but it isn't always normal. Disputes happen at work, home, and school because there's one truth we can't escape. Every person has their own opinion and no one can agree on everything. Sadly, unique people can never go through life without disagreement. Learning to resolve conflict and cope with the emotional side of it can certainly help you avoid it as much as you can. However, being in an abusive relationship where conflict is the order of the day doesn't mean you must stick around. You can walk away from something that causes you anxiety and brings no satisfaction.

Stress must be the most obvious trigger. Think about the route you take to work that causes you endless migraines. You can look for an alternative route to avoid the trigger. However, there are stressors we can't avoid, such as the death of your loved one, changing colleges, or relocating for work. The best you can do with natural stress is to learn how to cope with it. Most people will experience bouts of stress at some point. It will be reduced gradually with proper management.

Finances are another major trigger for most people at various times. Everything money related can increase your anxiety. The best way for you to cope with this trigger is to budget and plan every dollar spent. Invest in your future by saving money and planning for retirement. You can't avoid financial stress if your house floods, but you could avoid future incidents by learning how to manage money constructively. Commit to becoming a financially savvy person because even planning your retirement can be stressful. It's the only way you can lessen the blows from this trigger. Speaking to your employer about a raise is also not the worst idea once you're managing your anxiety and you can take extra responsibilities at work.

Personal triggers must be the most challenging kind. I try to think of them as being unnatural because someone with a severe phobia of staircases can't avoid them forever. All they can do is face the fear. Personal triggers either amp your anxiety up because of deep-seated fear, or they remind you of a traumatic memory. You have personal triggers if you suffer from PTSD. It isn't always cracking sounds or strobing lights that set you off. It can be the smell of a certain perfume that reminds you of someone you lost. It can be the taste of apple pie that brings back memories too. These triggers happen unconsciously in your mind, and they're hard to recognize.

Irrespective of what triggers you, most are better overcome than playing the avoidance game. For example, removing an alcoholic tendency is better than trying to silently avoid it. Learning to cope with your PTSD is better than trying to avoid the sound of misfired exhausts. You can only manage them by identifying them. That's how you gain coping mechanisms over time.

How to Identify Them

Some triggers will feel so natural or automatic that you can't see them. This is especially true for phobias, avoidance issues, and personal triggers. It won't take you one day to figure out what sets your anxiety off. Give yourself time to figure out what starts the feelings of dread. Use one of the four golden strategies, or combine them to recognize your triggers.

The first one is a promise you need to make to yourself. Be honest about what makes you feel uncomfortable. No one can judge you because you're doing this. I can't see your triggers and unless you share it with a therapist, no one will know about any you don't want to share out loud. Anxiety can cause you to assess yourself negatively and avoid giving yourself any credit where it's due. Don't fear your personal truth either because you can't lessen your anxiety if you deny the existence of certain triggers. Be the willing explorer of your private identification exercise until you feel safe sharing the results.

The second strategy is to use a journal so that you can recognize triggers you might've missed before. Your journal is as private as your honesty if you choose. Spend 10 minutes writing down your feelings when you feel implosive. Record the experience as best you can, leaving no details out. You might not be able to work through the emotions at the time and can always come back to find triggers later. What happened before you felt the way you did? What were the exact events that led up to your anxiety? Who was with you, where were you, and could the event have happened any other way?

The third strategy is to seek help if you can't identify your triggers alone. Therapy is a choice and you'll learn more about it in Chapter 10. There's no shame in talking to someone and seeking help so that you can start coping with these emotional shifts. Therapists are trained to help you deal with your problems. They know how to seek the triggers and can help anyone who can't identify it themselves.

Finally, you can become the investigator of the anxious experience with some directed thinking. Remember to diarize any epiphanies you stumble on. You'll need to ask yourself six questions when you feel scared in any situation.

1. What is going on around me at this present time?
2. What is going on in my thoughts while I stand here?
3. Am I even more worried now that my future, relatable experiences look bleeker?
4. Am I afraid of the physical sensations I feel in my body because they remind me of the last panic attack I had?
5. Does my possible inability to cope make me more nervous?
6. What are my expectations of myself and are they realistic?

Take all the time you need to list every trigger you can find. Record your answers in your journal and see who was around, where you were, and what you were thinking. The first question leads to a crucial answer. You need to try to remember every sensual stimulation during this exercise. How did you feel and was there any smell involved? You can also ask yourself these questions after experiencing an anxious event. It's best to practice it as early as possible and try to look at perspectives other than the thoughts in your mind. Pretend to be an outsider if you're recalling the experience later.

Managing your anxiety is much simpler once you have the triggers written down. Upcoming chapters will give you all the coping strategies you need, but for now, you want to find every trigger you can. It's up to you whether the trigger can be avoided or not. Circumstances might not allow avoidance and trying to prevent the triggers from occurring when you can't is a recipe for more anxiety. Some triggers are easy to avoid with some choice. You don't have to drink caffeine, and you needn't prepare for a speech if you're terrified of public speaking and your job allows you to work behind the scenes.

You don't need alcohol, caffeine, or unhealthy relationships if they only cause you anxiety. Social anxiety is more complicated and you'd be better off if you face your fear slowly. The other option is to decide which triggers you'll confront. For example, you might choose to face your public speaking fear. You could always join a group to gain experience and boost your confidence. Often, our fears are grounded in a lack of confidence when it comes to social and performance anxiety. The more we practice confidence, the better we resonate with it. This could help you overcome the fear of performing in front of a large crowd because you know you can do it.

Now that you have what you need to focus on, you can proceed to the anxiety management methods that will change your life for good.

Chapter 4:

Using Distraction for

Management

Distraction is a powerful tool for managing anxiety. Have you seen how paramedics encourage accident victims to keep talking to them? They ask them to tell them about their kids or something irrelevant to the accident. This doesn't only keep someone from falling asleep when shock consumes their energy and places them at risk for complications from a concussion. It also distracts them from the pain they're feeling. Anxiety and stress are painful and that's why you need this as your emergency strategy. You're about to learn about the advantages of distraction therapy and how to implement it when you become overwhelmed.

Why Choose a Distraction?

Distraction is useful for a range of mental health issues from the minor stress you want to avoid to a full-blown panic attack. Remember a time when you started cleaning your home or took a long walk because you felt unsure and needed time to think about something. There are simple forms of distraction that work for the mildest discomfort, but stronger methods can also be used for a multitude of reasons.

You can reflect your uneasy feelings into arts, craft, music, and any other talents you might have. This increases your creativity because you're getting extra practice by using your talents to distract your mind from unpleasant thoughts and feelings.

It can help you alleviate depression when you're feeling overwhelmed and need coping mechanisms besides drinking or other unhealthy strategies. The idea of distraction is that you'll be replacing unwanted feelings and thoughts with alternative emotions by focusing on something else. You have the benefit of relieving negative emotions that tear you up and rather put your mind into a positive activity.

Distraction methods can even subtly help you when you need rejuvenation bouts during the day. Losing energy can also cause us to feel more agitated even when we don't realize it. Many companies provide short tea breaks to their employees. The reason this works is that it gives them 10 minutes to be separate from work. Work is the minor stressor here and using these tiny top-ups throughout the day is what sees you through. It does wonders to do a short window-shopping excursion when you're feeling amped too.

Distraction is capable of guiding you away from self-harming thoughts, feeling depressed, and thinking that you have no control over the situation. Medical experts use it to calm panicked patients down and even combine it with other techniques, such as visualization, controlled breathing, and relaxation. The Journal of Behavioral Modification has published the results of a study that proves that therapist-guided distraction has worked (Hall & Lundh, 2018). Panic disorder patients were used in the study, and they showed significant coping strategies after only three sessions with a therapist. This proves that even the worst of anxiety can be targeted with distraction and that's what makes it so powerful for first-responders at accident scenes.

Distraction can bring you from the depths of the worst despair once you start using it. It should be practiced even when you're feeling well because your masterful usage will guarantee a calming effect when you experience panic attacks. It helps you manage mild to severe emotions and can be used anywhere, at any time. Distraction also doesn't erase the triggers that made you feel anxious, but it brings you to a calmer place where you have more strength to manage them. It moves your cognition from a hot spot to a cold process. We can't manage something rationally through emotional processing. We can awaken our logical minds once we calm the tantrum-throwing amygdala down. (Yes, I love calling the emotional center of the brain a child who throws tantrums!)

It's time for you to learn about the endless methods you can use to shift your focus from the painful experience to a place where you can find a resolution.

Subtle Distractions

Using simpler distractions can be great when you're in the middle of your working day or at a family gathering. You don't want to draw too much attention and would rather use subtle distractions to calm your mind down quickly. Heck, you can even use some of them while driving as long as your attention can be shared with the road. Pulling over isn't a bad idea either. The subtle distractions might not be the best option for explosive anxiety, but they work when you need to remove yourself from the current situation for five minutes to decrease your heart rate and think about things rationally.

You can stroke or cuddle a pet if you're at someone's home. It looks so natural and no one will know better.

Take a quick tea break at work or home if you feel anxious. Excuse yourself if people are around and make yourself a calming tea. Any hot drink will work, but make sure it's decaffeinated if you're going for coffee. I recommend two kinds of tea. The first is valerian root tea because it can rapidly reduce symptoms of anxiety (Benke et al., 2009). It releases a potent chemical called gamma-aminobutyric acid (GABA) which is like a natural calming drug that your brain normally provides in happy experiences. The second hot drink is any green tea. Green tea releases a hormone called L-theanine amino acid that forces the mind and body to relax (Finglas, n.d.). Tea breaks will have a new meaning now.

You can also take a walk through a park you enjoy. Try to focus on what's going on around you in the park during your walk.

Music is another soul-soother, but you must listen to calming music and not punk-rock or heavy metal. Music has a way of guiding your mood in both good and bad ways. Avoid music that makes you sad or speeds your thoughts up.

Exercise is a great method for combating anxiety bouts. It's also known to release feel-good chemicals when you go for a jog, do some relaxing stretches, or hit the gym. Many people use yoga and tai chi for relaxation purposes but your activity will depend on what you love doing. Distractions won't work unless you choose an option that you enjoy. We'll cover exercise in more detail later.

Reading is another option you can try; what could make you get lost in another reality more than a great book? Choose a book that draws you in from the first word, one that makes you think wow every time you turn a page.

Writing and journaling is another simple strategy for dealing with anxiety as you've already learned. It also doubles as a distraction method.

Coloring in adult pictures has amazing soothing abilities. It requires a keen focus to turn that black and white mandala into something that bursts with the colors that you love. Adult coloring books and smartphone apps are becoming more and more popular.

Using your talents or hobbies to distract yourself is another awesome subtle strategy. Watching something be created from nothing is calming to the mind. Try painting a picture, playing an instrument, or drawing something from your imagination.

Netflix offers you some distracting options as well because it just keeps going to the next episode and works for anyone who wants to use binge-watching for calming themselves down. Any television program or movie will work. However, anything you watch, read, or listen to must be positive. Avoid any programs that make you cry, or upset you in any way.

Video games are also distracting even though we relate them to kids. The fact that you can control what happens in the game gives you some sense of agency back when you feel like you're losing it.

The final subtle technique is as simple as calling or visiting a friend. Social interactions might be triggers for you, but you can't deny that being close to your good friend makes the world seem less scary. The only secret with using this distraction is that you aren't calling them to unload your anxiety over the phone. Ruminating on your pains won't make them hurt any less. Remember that distraction means that you must remove yourself from the hurtful emotions until your cold cognitions are functioning again. This means that you must only call your friend to relax your mind and listen to their voice. Don't even ask them for advice at that moment. Simply ask them how their day has been and what they plan to do this coming weekend.

These give you amazing options when you feel nervous about meeting a new blind date at a friend's house. You can pet the dog and have a cup of tea. Are you feeling anxious while driving? Turn the volume up on an audiobook or listen to your favorite song that brings happy memories back.

"I Need More Distraction"

There's nothing wrong with needing more and there are a few great techniques you can use when you feel panic setting in. I already mentioned that distraction combined with other techniques works for professional therapists. You can create more structured and focused distractions for times you need more than a puppy kiss. Intense anxiety won't always be resolved by coloring a picture. There are three stronger techniques you can use when the intensity is insane.

The first one is where you deliberately replace negative emotions with positive ones. Overwhelming emotions can hit you like a speeding train. Stop everything you're busy with and immediately bring your heart rate down by watching a hilarious movie when you feel angry. Read funny greeting cards at the drugstore when you feel sad. Read a life-affirming book as soon as the thoughts of depression and worthlessness get too much. The goal is to replace your current emotion with anything that immediately gives you the opposite reaction. A comedy can get you laughing. Heck, watch kittens on YouTube when you feel depressed. Get yourself laughing because we never forget how to laugh even in our deepest agony.

The second distraction method for all-consuming anxiety is to get out there and help someone else. It shifts your attention from your problems to theirs. It's also quite an emotional accomplishment when you share positive activities with someone else who needs it. Volunteer at the animal or homeless shelter, donate clothes you don't use to a charity store, or give something to another person. Surprise someone with a gift or by doing the unexpected. Sharing positive emotions is a powerful distraction for you. Spreading kindness and generosity can also make you see all the things you can be grateful for in your life.

Positive imagery is a good strategy and can be practiced on your own or guided by an application like *Headspace*. You can even opt for a therapist that guides you to a positive, safe, happy, and favorable image in your mind. You can close your eyes, breathe evenly, and imagine a memory that carries joy for you. Breathing is essential to creating a relaxed state of mind and allowing your diaphragm to receive the oxygen it needs. Slow and even breaths are encouraged. Go to any place, previously visited or one on your bucket list. Waterfalls, landscapes, beaches, forests, mountains, and any place you desire will work. You can imagine people being with you or you can be alone.

The reason you're imagining a mental image is so that you can replace negative and emotional thoughts with something new until you have more strength to face the problem. Immerse yourself entirely into the image and allow yourself to hear, see, feel, smell, and taste what you create in your mind. You want to relax those flurry emotions even when you experience agoraphobia or breathlessness. You'll also feel safer in this mental space until you calm down. Focus on relaxing your muscles and allow the image to consume you. You're welcome to use guided imagery or you can create an image that suits your preferences better.

I've included a brief, guided distraction exercise for you. Enjoy what I've created or you can customize it to suit you. Customizing visualizations can also boost your creativity as talents do. However, some people need a little practice before they can do this alone. That's why I recommend guided imagery until you get the hang of it. Remember to practice distracting visualizations daily so that you can slip into one whenever you need it. Find a place where you're most comfortable and remove any restrictive clothing, noises, and hindrances from your imagery space. Lie down or sit up if you must; you just need to be comfortable.

A Journey to Peru

Make yourself as comfortable as you can and close your eyes as you take a deep breath. Wait a moment before you release the air and feel the way it tickles your nostrils upon its exit. Take another breath and focus on the way this fresh air fills your lungs. Take one more breath and feel how your chest rises gently while the air reaches the deepest parts of your body. Continue breathing as you shift your focus to your muscles. Do they feel tense? Where do they feel tense? Your breathing remains even as you focus on giving your muscles permission to relax now. It doesn't happen all at once, but rather slowly. Every breath that leaves your body is taking some tension out of your muscles.

Remain in this state until your body feels less stressed. Allow my voice and these words to guide the evenness of your breaths and each ounce of tension that creeps out of your body. Don't let any thoughts enter your mind yet. You're only focusing on your relaxation for now. Take another deeper breath and permit that knotty feeling in your stomach to subside. Is it still there? Take another breath and focus on how the knot unravels before it flows out of your body.

Now, I want you to listen to me carefully. I want you to draw a picture. You can allow my picture to become yours or you can use one of your own. Your body has finally become weightless and now you can take yourself to your space that brings utter peace to you.

I'm going to go to a memorable place in Peru. There's a beautiful place called the rainbow mountains in the Andes Mountain Range. It's the most incredible place you can imagine. Allow yourself to arrive slowly as it takes time to reach it on horseback. Feel the movements of the horse as it carries you closer to the most incredible thing you'll ever see. Can you smell the horse? Listen to the people traveling with you if there are any. Who is with you on this journey? How close are you to them? Allow their voices to be a distant reminder of how much they mean to you. You can feel the air changing as you approach higher ground on the horse that's body movements are conforming to your comfort.

Bring your focus back to your body momentarily and notice how relaxed you feel once more. When last have you truly felt this way? Okay, go back to your journey now. You can hear the laughter of people you love who are traveling with you. Allow their joy to become yours and bring the rhythm of the horse to your attention again. You've become one with the horse and its freedom belongs to you. Your thoughts and imagination are guiding it to the peak where you'll see the mountains. Feel the air brush past your face as you take the next step onto the peak. You've arrived at the most beautiful and natural painting the world has to give.

Look at the mountains and the way they curve with colors you didn't think were possible in nature. The orange is as bright as the sun, and the red makes you feel warmth. The blue lines running through the hills are stirring a deeper peace within you. How can nature that's so beautiful not be experienced? Dismount the horse now and sit on the peak. Allow anyone with you to sit next to you. Feel their hand as they enjoy the colorful rainbow with you. The ebb and flow of the colors bring about positive emotions. You can feel happiness, joy, and peace flow in every inch of your body. Take every moment of this spectacular image into your mind. Welcome it to your deepest parts of the body.

Keep sitting on the peak until you feel like nothing can break this image. Remain in the peace you've created and partake in the freedom it brings your mind. You're welcome to stay here as long as you want. When you're ready to come back, you can shift your attention slowly to your breath again. Only come back when you're ready. Focusing on your breath and counting to ten will help you return to your visualization space. Don't rush if you're loving your creation. Memories are meant to be savored and even imagined creations can be immersive.

When you do come back, just remain in your physical space for a moment as you feel how your body and mind have reached a higher peace that you never thought possible.

Distracting yourself with positive imagery is something you can do anywhere daily. Use my session as inspiration to create your own, and you can move on to the next anxiety management tool when you're ready.

Chapter 5:

Breathing Exercises are

Another Management Tool

Breathing is the life source of the body and mind, and using the right type will make the difference between experiencing a panic attack and calming yourself down. You can't survive without oxygen, obviously. However, incorrect breathing can make matters worse instead of helping you. People with anxiety need to learn how to breathe so that all the tension can dissipate. You'll find multiple breathing techniques to help you stop a panic attack from happening.

The Function of Breath

Breathing exercises are one of the simplest forms of stress reduction and anxiety relaxation. It calms your body once you learn how to use them, and then you have one more tool in your anxiety management box. The rhythm and biological structure of correcting your breath at a time of desperate need is hugely beneficial to your mental, emotional, and overall well-being. The body is a simple system if you know how to manage it correctly. Our muscles tense up when we become anxious and the stress response triggers the defense mode. These muscles need oxygen and the nutrients they receive with it. Relaxed muscles will also decrease elevated blood pressure because the heart is a muscle after all. A tense heart will pump blood too fast and push your blood pressure to a new record high.

The balance of oxygen in your body can also improve concentration because let's face it, sometimes you'll need a keen focus to decide what comes next when your breathing has already taken a turn for the worst. Evening out your breath can help carry oxygen to every cell in your body to prevent brain cells from misfiring when you need them to work. The truth is that you're taking more oxygen in than releasing air when you hyperventilate. The body wasn't built for this reaction, and stress should always be kept to the minimum. Compare your body to an engine once more.

You can't buy a new car, push it to the extreme limits, avoid servicing it, and then expect it to run until it hits 50,000 miles on the odometer. Breathing exercises are like the service intervals your body requires when it's working overtime.

I mentioned two kinds of breathing in Chapter Two. The thoracic kind and diaphragm breathing. Remember that diaphragm breathing is when oxygen reaches the deepest core of your body. It's often described as abdominal breathing. Thoracic breathing is a genuine threat to the human body (Ankrom & Morin, 2019). One of the reasons why breathing rapidly into the chest area alone and pushing it out before it reaches the organs is that oxygen is collected by your cells and carbon dioxide isn't released fast enough. Carbon dioxide is a dangerous chemical and the body needs to excrete it. The only way it can do this is through the breath that leaves your body. So, there isn't enough time for the cells in your body to release the poison when you're breathing rapidly.

An upset exchange between oxygen and carbon dioxide is what ultimately causes a panic attack when cells are poisoned, and they aren't receiving the oxygen they need to recycle. Every organ in your body, including your brain, heart, kidneys, liver, and lungs are made of cells. This fact alone is why learning to breathe correctly with your diaphragm is how you protect yourself from severe anxiety. It becomes a worsened danger when anxious people don't even notice the shallow, short, and rapid breaths before they go numb or feel dizzy. It's easy for this person to feel sick and become even more anxious when they're about to faint. Unfortunately, their breath becomes more strained as they fear the impending attack.

The body automatically responds by defending itself from danger. Your heart rate speeds up, your muscles become tense, and you can actually faint when carbon dioxide levels have reached an uncontrollable presence in the brain. The starved brain will switch you off when you faint so that it can rejuvenate breathing itself. I know that this sounds frightening, but take a gentle breath right now and recognize that awareness of the dangers is better than denying it. You're about to learn how to use diaphragmatic breathing to prevent this problem from ever causing you emotional anguish again. Start your lessons by testing your breath right now.

Put one hand on your chest and place the other one on your upper abdomen as you take 10 gentle and even breaths.

Determine whether your chest or upper abdomen rises more. The abdomen will expand and contract more than your chest if you're breathing with your diaphragm. The hand on your chest shouldn't rise more than your abdomen. This would indicate that you're breathing thoracically.

Do this exercise now and see how you normally breathe. Then I want you to examine your breathing the next time you feel even slightly anxious. Recognizing the problem and using corrective breathing when you're apprehensive will certainly help you calm down. It reforms the balance between oxygen and carbon dioxide. There's only one more piece of advice I can give you before you start training. This takes practice and you should start at home in your free time. You don't even have to be anxious to practice it. Practice will make sure you can implement your chosen strategy when you are dealing with an anxiety episode.

The Multitude of Exercises Available

Several breathing exercises can help calm you down once you've practiced them. Who knew that people could breathe in so many ways? However, it certainly helps you to choose one that works for you. Try each one until you find the technique that you can use anywhere and at any time. Focus intensely on what you're doing because we can still breathe incorrectly, until we get the knack of it.

Elongated Exits

Deep breaths aren't the only form of correction you can use. It might not work for you because inhaling is connected to the sympathetic nervous system that controls your stress response, and exhaling is controlled by the parasympathetic nervous system that controls your relaxation (Gotter & Legg, 2019). Therefore, you might be taking too much breath in and not releasing enough of the recycled gas.

Breathing never sounded complicated before because it's how we live every day. It still isn't complex but the reason for using the elongated exit strategy is that some anxious people don't even realize that their breathing is a problem until they experience panic. This method is used when you want to reverse the process of taking in too much oxygen and not releasing the bad stuff.

Once you're ready to try this technique, you can find any position that's comfortable for you. Use beats to count your inhale and exhale periods. A single beat is as long as you find it comfortable. It could be two seconds long or four if you can manage this. Keep your beats shorter when you start practicing this method. However long your beats are, you'll have a rest period which lasts for four beat counts, or a relax period that lasts for five beats. Allow your body to guide you to find your beating rhythm. It isn't advised to follow your heartbeats, especially if your heart is pumping erratically. Rather count your beats and follow the exercise. You can start now:

Exhale for two beats before you begin so that you can press any unwanted air out first.

Take your first breath without forcing it and count one beat.

Exhale gently while counting two beats.

Repeat the inhale for one beat and then exhale for two beats.

Take a rest period where you count four beats.

Inhale for one beat and exhale for two beats again.

Take your relaxation period now by counting five beats.

Continue inhaling for one beat and exhaling for two beats.

Maintain your rest and relax counts in between.

Try to stick with the exercise for at least five minutes per session.

Belly Breathing

Belly breathing is an exercise where you force your diaphragm to do the work. This method ensures even breathing and it gives you a focal point when you learn how to visualize properly. You'll want to lie down for this one, and place pillows under your knees and head. You can also sit if you prefer, but your head, neck, and shoulders must be relaxed with your knees bent slightly upward. You'll also place one hand over your heart and the other one just under your rib cage. It's best to use your nose for inhaling and exhaling with this one. Your goal is to make your stomach expand instead of your chest region. Let's do this:

Position yourself as you find best and place your hands in their required regions.

You're going to focus on taking 10 gentle and even breaths through your nose.

Notice whether your abdominal or chest hand is rising more than the other one.

Your belly won't move alone, but it must expand more than the rest of your body.

You can purse your lips and gently exhale through your mouth if you choose.

Take it slow and steady.

Try using your stomach muscles to gently push the air out of your diaphragm.

You want all the bad air gone and then take another even breath through your nose.

Continue doing this for at least 10 breaths.

Focal Breathing

This method uses specific deep breathing that guarantees you won't sustain bad air in your lungs. You'll notice that every guided meditation or visualization you find always defaults to using deeper breaths. It works but only if you follow the rules of this exercise. Even I use deep breathing to guide someone but I strictly remind them to push the air out gently. You want to empty your lungs every time you breathe out. So, remember this when you listen to my journey to Peru again.

Deep breathing can only work if it's focused and slow. The length of your breath will depend on what's comfortable for you, but try to make them last long enough to press all the air out. You can use mouth or nose breathing. You can lie down or sit for this exercise. This sample exercise will use a lying position because it adds some exhale strategies. Shall we begin?

Lie down on a comfortable surface and use your elbows to raise your chest.

Gently press the air out of your lungs before you retreat to the surface again.

Focus on your breathing now that you've excreted unwanted air.

You might notice tension in your muscles that wasn't even recognizable before.

Simply listen to your breath for 30 seconds before you take a gentle breath in.

Watch your body expand and fall flat as you slowly prolong your exhalation.

Take another gentle but controlled deep breath in and count to three.

Press the air out slowly and make sure your lungs are empty before taking three seconds rest again.

Take another deep breath and control its entry.

Watch your body rise again and you can push yourself up on your elbows once more.

Hold your position for two seconds and start pressing the air out before you fall flat again.

Keep doing this and focusing on how the clean air makes you feel calmer. You can also add an inner mantra every time you draw another breath. Repeat the word calmness or peace as you breathe in. You want to imagine the negative air leaving your body while you exhale as well.

Breathing Equilibrium

The ancient pranayama practitioners of yoga have another great exercise you can use. This one is simple, as long as you maintain the same length of inhalations and exhalations. It's also better known as "even breathing" and is taught in most yogic practices. You can lie down or sit as long as you find your best comfortable position. Time each breath in and out for four seconds. Let's see the method in action:

Position yourself comfortably and just listen to your current breathing for a few cycles.

Feel the air as it passes in and out of your lungs.

Keep paying attention to your breathing but don't control it yet as you close your eyes.

Allow yourself to feel and experience each breath that passes.

Now, you can take a gentle and unforced breath into your nose.

Count to four while you're drawing the breath in.

You can feel your diaphragm rising.

Now, count to four again as you release the breath as gently as you took it in.

Your inhale and exhale must be four seconds each.

Continue breathing in while counting and releasing the air for another four seconds.

Pay attention to the way your body fills up when you inhale and feel the emptiness when you exhale.

Breathing Resonantly

This exercise is particularly useful to calm an anxious body down. You'll lie down and close your eyes before starting. You want to reach a relaxed state of mind and this is best done in a horizontal position. Your focus must be on the feelings of your body as you breathe in and out. You want to feel the lungs fill and empty with each round. Let's do this:

Find your position and close your eyes and mouth.

Breathe in slowly through your nose for six seconds without forcing it.

Gentle inhaling is the best for this exercise. You aren't filling your lungs to their maximum capacity.

Release the air gently through your nose for another six seconds without forcing it.

Maintain this breathing for 10 minutes or more if you need to. Never allow your focus to shift away from the feelings your body is sharing with you.

Alternate Nostril Breathing

This is another great exercise that hails from the yogic pranayama culture. Yoga has been a great management tool for anxiety and this is simply one more breathing technique it offers. You'll need to sit for this one because you must straighten your spine and raise your forehead to open your respiratory system properly.

Push your chest forward gently without bending your spine. You'll leave your left hand resting in your lap and raise the right hand. Place your index and middle fingers against your forehead and let them rest there. You want your resting fingers to touch down between your eyebrows. You're going to close your eyes and use your nose for breathing with this exercise. Let's see how it works:

Get into the prescribed position and feel your body rest like this while you're breathing normally.

Now, take your thumb from the resting forehead hand and cover your right nostril.

Take a gentle and slow breath through the left nostril and hold it.

Bring your ring finger down to pinch your nose closed entirely for a brief moment.

Lift your thumb and allow the ring finger to keep the left nostril closed.

Gently press the air out through the right nostril now.

Pause for a moment before you inhale gently through the right nostril again.

Pause for another brief moment after pressing both nostrils closed again.

Raise your ring finger this time and slowly exhale through the left nostril.

Repeat the cycles for 10 breaths in and out while each alternating breath should last about 40 seconds in total.

I know this one is hard to practice, but it truly opens your diaphragm up for receiving oxygen. It also allows you to practice both nostrils for a more intense breathing exercise.

Lion's Breath

The final breathing exercise you can learn is another fascinating one from pranayama yoga. It's also not for the faint-hearted and requires dedicated practice. Similar to the previous technique, it guides you into a yoga position that opens your diaphragm to receiving more oxygen and expelling carbon dioxide. Yoga does that.

Yoga practitioners believe that we have chakras and in simple terms, these chakras connect one major organ to the next. The heart is a chakra and the core or diaphragm is another one.

Let's see how flexible you are in opening your full respiratory system with a pose intended for breathing better. You can practice in the same position as alternate nostril breathing if you're too uncomfortable at first. The method also allows you to use a mantra that vibrates throughout your respiratory system to increase muscle relaxation. Here we go:

Enter a kneeling position where you cross your ankles and rest on the bottom of your feet.

Stretch your arms and fingers to loosen them and rest them on your knees.

Breathe in deeply but gently through your nose.

Exhale gently through your mouth while you slowly create the sound 'ha.'

Elongate your mantra as the breath leaves your body slowly and steadily.

Open your mouth widely and stick your tongue out while you gently press the air and mantra out.

Try to focus on your forehead or the tip of your nose as you exhale.

Stop and relax your face muscles as you inhale slowly and gently again.

No mantra is needed when you inhale.

Repeat this exercise three times before uncrossing your ankles and switching their position to the opposite side. Do it for another three breaths while continuing your focus on your nasal tip and extending the mantra for ultimate results.

Breathing corrections will help you manage your anxiety by keeping your body at its peak function. Some require little practice and others might need some time to master. Moreover, these methods can be integrated into other anxiety management tools, so don't give up until you get it right.

Chapter 6:

Successful Progressive

Muscle Relaxation: How

and Why

Progressive muscle relaxation is another great anxiety-ridding tool. Have you ever felt the freedom of being so relaxed after a massage that you become blended into the surface beneath you? The way a massage therapist guides the tension out of your muscles and the feeling of letting go of sensations you carry with you is best experienced. However, you might be someone who had anxiety for such a long time that you don't know anything other than the tension that exists in your muscles. You aren't even aware of it anymore because we get used to feeling certain things. Rigidity isn't only released by massage therapists; it can be done at home too.

What Is It?

Progressive muscle relaxation (PMR) is what you use when you need to learn how to relax. Anyone anxious for a long time will forget how to relax every muscle in their body. They'll forget what relaxation means. Physician Edmund Jacobson noticed an unwelcoming trend among patients in the 1920s, irrespective of what their ailment was (Star & Gans, 2019). He knew that muscles contracted when the person became anxious, but in many cases, patients were ill and suffering from aching muscles that weren't necessarily part of their ailment. Our muscles tense up when we reach the fight or flight response, even if we don't need them to survive because there is no threat to our life or well-being.

Muscle tension is simply part of the preservation of our bodies and it still happens even if we don't recognize how rigid we become. Jacobson started experimenting on his patients to see if he could teach them how to control their muscle tension. The truth, especially for those of us who don't realize how our bodies contract, is that we must practice tensing and releasing our muscles so that we can gain the awareness we need to relax them. You can learn how to control the rigidity and unfold a calm, relaxed state where the pains and tensions subside. Jacobson developed PMR after realizing that it could give ill or anxious people their control back. It allows them to let go of the physical reaction brought on by their stress.

This simple and progressive method of releasing the tension that builds in our muscles has alleviated many problems associated with anxiety. Firstly, it reduces your stress and that automatically lessens the blow. PMR can also help you sleep better and combat insomnia related to your fears or concerns. It teaches you to tense your muscles, focus on the sensation of this, and release the rigidity before you notice how much better that muscle group feels. Some people prefer to practice PMR while sitting because it can lead to falling asleep, especially if you've been anxious so long that your body was crying for a calmer state. This anxiety tool can even help with body image issues because you become familiar with a body that was once alien.

These exercises can help you relieve pain related to anxiety and reduce stiffness that could rather lead to further injury. Stunt doubles can tell you a tale that makes you understand what PMR does. They don't tense their muscles before falling because this can lead to injuries. Instead, they allow their muscles to become limp and the impact is reduced. You might even learn about this fact when you do team-building exercises at work. The trust fall doesn't work as well when you plank your body. The intention is that you trust your colleague and fall limply into their arms. Relaxation also brings your heart rate down and calms a mind that wants to hop all over the place.

Your physical and mental well-being are improved as you've already learned how the stress response can alter your health. You reduce these risks when you learn to relax. The advantages of PMR are countless, and there's only one secret to making it work. You must start practicing it today so that it comes naturally when you feel anxious again. Dedicate 15 minutes daily to practicing any of the PMR exercises for two weeks. It's difficult to implement it for the first time when you enter a panic attack. Indeed, it can help you traverse and avoid a panic attack because your breathing and heart rate will calm down before your oxygen levels are unbalanced. It takes practice though and you can start before you feel anxious. Practice it while you feel relaxed so that it's easier to recognize the changes in your muscles.

Guidelines to Learn

Learning PMR is simple if you follow some rules during the exercises. You must start with a breathing exercise. I use the breathing equilibrium concept to make sure my breaths are even. Other people start with deep breathing, but you must ensure elongated exhalations if you choose this one. Use the breathing technique you're most comfortable with. Avoid complicated methods from the pranayama.

Breathing is a check and the next requirement for PMR is that you choose a practice arena where you won't be disturbed. Your comfort is always important and noisy distractions aren't the best to have around. Use a comfortable armchair or you can lie down if you think you won't fall asleep.

The third tip is that you must focus on your body's sensations throughout the exercise. Notice how your muscles feel when you inhale and pull them tight. Pay attention to the muscle groups as you release the tension because you need to learn what relaxation feels like. You won't be learning the differences if you aren't focusing on your body while you do PMR.

You can also choose to use the tense and release PMR tactic if you're practicing the method beforehand so that you grow accustomed to the sensations. However, you can skip the tensing of muscles if you're feeling a little stressed and want to practice relaxation alone.

One major rule that many people dismiss is that we cannot tense and release painful muscles. This exercise should never cause more pain. Practice it without focusing on the region where you have an injury. For example, you won't be tensing and releasing your fist if you broke a finger.

Finally, you can work your way up or down. You can start with your face or your feet, depending on what makes you more comfortable. You can also focus on larger muscle groups before targeting a specific one. Maybe you don't have much control over practicing your muscles in the toes alone yet, and then you can start with your entire foot. You'll become an expert PMR practitioner and will move on to specific groups with time. Let's take a look at some groups you need to learn about and how they can be pulled tightly before we dive into the exercises.

You can curl your toes downward to tense your feet. Tightening the calf muscles is as simple as pulling your toes upwards towards you. Applying the upward or downward motion of the toes with pulling your thighs tight will tense your entire leg. It's best to focus on one leg at a time and move to the other one when you're done with the first. Your hands are the easiest place to tense muscles if you clench your fists. Your arms are also easy because you can raise your hand to your shoulder and clench your fist to make a strongman position. Your arms must also be exercised individually.

Pulling your buttocks tight is fun and simple as well. Your stomach will tense up if you pull it in. Your chest might seem like a hard one but taking a deep breath expands the diaphragm and allows the muscles to pull tighter. You can pull your shoulders up to touch your ears as this will work for your neck and shoulder tightening. Your mouth is another muscle group and you can open it wide as though you're yawning big enough to swallow a house. Tense your upper face by shutting your eyelids tight or raising your eyebrows as high as they can go.

Going into any exercise now will require each muscle group to be pulled tight for 10 seconds unless I specify otherwise. Remember all the rules and let's see how your definition of relaxation changes now.

PMR Exercises

These exercises are for you if you don't have a willing partner who can massage every muscle into submission. Besides, you need to practice these methods because your partner, massage therapist, or handy self-massaging electronic gadget isn't always available when you feel anxious. You want to be in control when anxiety hits and you can do it by learning to control your muscles intentionally.

Quickie PMR

Quick "life hacks" are life's tiny pleasures, including relaxation exercises. This exercise will help you if you don't have time to spend 15 minutes in your routine. It also helps when you aren't in the best place to start shutting down. Because this is a quick exercise, you can focus on each step for 30 seconds. Let's do this.

Lift your shoulders high enough to be above your chin or near your ears.

Turn your head to the right and hold the position for 15 seconds before turning your head to the left to hold for another 15 seconds.

Relax your shoulders and feel the tension leave your neck.

Stretch your arms out straight and clench your fists. Hold this position for 30 seconds.

Feel the sensation of the arm muscles before releasing it. Focus on how good the relaxation feels upon the release.

Squeeze your butt muscles and hold for 30 seconds, paying attention to the feelings.

Release the tension and notice how great it feels.

Stand on your tiptoes and pull those leg muscles tight. Hold this for 30 seconds or longer if you can manage before it cramps up.

Release and exhale for three seconds as you notice how your legs feel free from the tension now.

Spend 30 seconds longer in your standing position so that you can focus on the sensations in your relaxed body. Start from the beginning if your muscles are still tense anywhere.

Self-Massage

This is another quick fix but it isn't advised in the middle of a public space. Your colleagues might think you're weird if you're massaging your own back in the boardroom. The name says it all, but you can follow some guidelines.

Sit down on a comfortable surface.

Start by raising your hands to your neck and rubbing it from the inside out. Your elbows will point outward.

Next, roll the balls of your feet into the ground as though you're kneading dough.

Fold your upper body over gently and rest your abdomen on your legs.

Massage your calves in a rolling ball format again while keeping your back rested to avoid injury.

Finally, stand up and use the same circular motions to massage your lower back.

Head to Toes

Progressive muscle relaxation is also great to start practicing with guided sessions. The first method you can try is working your way from your forehead down to your toes. Are you ready?

Sit in a comfortable chair which allows you to sink into it once you're relaxed.

Start with your spine straight and take even breaths. Five breath cycles are good to start with and you can make sure every exhale is as effective as your intake.

Close your eyes if this helps you stay focused on your breathing and sensations.

Feel your diaphragm rise with every breath you take in and shift your attention to your forehead.

Raise your eyebrows as high as you can and hold it for 10 seconds. Can you feel the tension building in your face?

Now, release the hold and focus intently on the way the muscles feel after the tension leaves them.

Open your mouth wide and stretch it a little. Notice how it's pulling your cheeks tighter.

Don't forget to breathe throughout the exercise. Try to maintain even breaths if you can.

Release your jaw with a gentle but slow exhale of breath. Your cheeks should feel more relaxed now.

Raise your shoulders as high as possible and hold them.

Continue slow and even breaths as you feel the neck and shoulders carry more weight.

Drop them abruptly as you exhale so that you can feel the tension push its way out forcefully.

Raise your right arm into a strongman position and clench your fist tight. Hold it for 10 seconds and pay attention to the pressure building in your biceps. Keep your fist straight and don't bend it. This isn't necessary. Pop your fist open when you exhale and feel the tension flee from your fingertips. Drop your arm down with the next breath that leaves your body and feel it become like jelly next to your body again.

Do five more clenches with your right fist, without taking your focus away from how your fingers feel lighter with each release.

Raise your left arm into the strongman position and clench your left fist. Hold the position and pay attention to the pressure building around your bicep again. Allow your fist to pop open abruptly when you exhale and feel the electrical energy leave it. Take another breath in and push it out gradually as you drop your left arm to your side again.

You want to do another five clenches with your left fist while paying attention to the energy released with each sudden opening.

Now, draw a deeper breath into your chest and hold it. Allow the air to remain there for a brief moment before pushing the tension out with your next exhale. Repeat the chest area to make sure you get all the tension out of your muscles if you can't hold your breath long enough. Make sure your exhalation is ridding your body of all the bad oxygen with a long and even push outwards.

Move on to your stomach region now and pull those muscles tighter. Can you feel the pressure it places on the entire core muscle system? Hold it there and keep breathing gently but evenly as you maintain the position. The pressure is quite strong in the core muscles of your body. Feel the sensations as you abruptly release your hold on another exhale. This pop will come with much tension release and you can even repeat it if there isn't full relaxation in the stomach region.

Your buttocks is next and you'll clench it as though you're trying to impress a partner with a tight one. You'll feel your body rise and you need to continue breathing evenly. Feel how tight those muscles get before you pop them loose and let go of the tension during an exhalation. Your bottom feels lighter and you can repeat the tightening once more if you need to.

Now, stretch your right leg forwards and pull it tight. Allow your upper thigh to feel the tension. Hold the position as you focus on those pressurized sensations. Don't let your leg cramp up but keep breathing evenly as you hold it in the air. Your toes are pointed outwards like a ballerina. Drop your leg back to the ground abruptly and focus on the relaxation in your thigh.

Place the ball of your right foot on the ground and raise your toes towards you. This will pull the calf muscle tight. Hold it for 10 seconds and release the foot downwards to feel the amazing relaxation in the calf muscle.

Now, curl your right toes to the ground and hold it again as you keep breathing evenly. Can you feel the tension in the bridge of your foot? Loosen the foot suddenly on another exhale and move your focus to your left side.

Raise your left leg and point those toes as a ballerina would again. Hold this position as you feel the upper thigh pull tight. You aren't doing it right if you can't feel the pressure in your thigh. Then you need to raise it higher. Drop it suddenly and notice how the thigh feels lighter now.

Knead the ball of your foot into the ground again and raise those toes towards you. Feel your left calf muscle strain itself. It has so much tension. Hold for 10 seconds and drop it abruptly. The entire calf feels more relaxed now.

Finally, curl your left toes towards you and focus on the feeling in your left foot. Release it suddenly after the hold and notice how your bridge feels relaxed.

Don't move immediately after your exercise. Rather sit there, scanning your body to pay attention to the incredible way it feels when you're relaxed.

That concludes the 15-minute exercise for each major muscle group. You can reverse the exercise if you prefer to start at the toes. You can also lie down but it won't be as effective. Lastly, you can skip all the tension and simply scan your body for pressure that you intentionally release using the same method. Practice your chosen method of PMR at least once daily and you'll have another great tool for anxious times. Yoga and tai chi also teach PMR techniques, if you'd like to join a class.

Chapter 7:

How to Use Grounding

Techniques to Keep

Anxiety at Bay

Have you ever felt detached from what's going on around you? Your mind becomes distant and the voices from your friends are moving further away. Anxiety is known for removing us from the only place we can make a difference. It takes us away from the only place we can enjoy our lives and cope with stress. The present moment is where reality and coping abilities exist, and learning to ground yourself in it is the next anxiety management tool you need to adopt.

Grounding Benefits

Grounding yourself might seem like common sense to some people, but you know how complex everything seems when your thoughts are speeding through your mind. The truth is that we tend to leave reality when we become overwhelmed. This happens to everyone who enters an anxious state or experiences panic. You hear bad news or anything that acts as a trigger and the response starts in your brain. Your heart rate increases and sounds become distant. This is also often seen in shock when someone stares off into nothingness. At this point, you might feel detached from your body, reality, or the people around you. Anxiety, especially panic, dissociates you from the present moment.

Reality can only exist here and now. It can't live in tomorrow or yesterday. However, someone who suffers from PTSD could suddenly be triggered and get lost in the memories that hurt them deeply. Entering a panic attack can also bring flashbacks and negative thinking that separates your fast-moving mind from your body. You might even think you've left your body behind. You can't attach yourself to the surrounding environment. Minor stressors and severe triggers could set off a chain reaction in your body that makes you struggle to connect with your mind. You battle to control your thoughts and your body goes into limbo. It could even happen when you realize that you have stress headed your way.

Anxiety removes you from the present and unfortunately, you can't deal with anxious thoughts if you aren't partaking presently in them. Grounding doesn't only bring you back to the present, but it also reconnects your mind and body so that you can cope with immediate problems. Admittedly, you'll become anxious for reasons that might be genuinely threatening. You can't react to it if you're frozen either. You need your senses intact and then you can find a solution.

According to Therapist Joanna Filidor, grounding is used to prevent severe reactions to stress and anxiety (Deering, 2020). It can stop the shell shock experienced by PTSD sufferers, painful flashbacks, and panic attacks. You reconnect to your body while separating yourself from the emotional turmoil.

Grounding can help you reduce extreme levels of anxiety or simple stress. It can even relieve the brain fog we experience in depression. We can regain our focus on what's happening right now, and remove the distractions that trigger us. This management tool can also help you calm down when your mind stops racing and you can think without emotions. There are many ways to ground yourself when you feel the overwhelming feelings creep up on you. All the strategies have one thing in common, though. You must use your five senses to bring yourself out of the dissociation and back into your present environment.

Focusing intently on your breathing is a form of grounding. The breathing equilibrium works well for this blended method too. Stretching and exercising give you some leverage as well because you're focusing on your body's movement sensations. Anything you can feel, see, hear, smell, and taste will help you come back from panic and allow you to address the problem. You can use simple grounding for minor stress, such as taking a sensual walk. The rule to remember with grounding is that it also takes practice as any self-help exercises do. You should start practicing your chosen techniques today and don't wait until you're anxious before you implement it.

Once you know how many ways you can ground yourself, the simpler it becomes to practice it multiple times daily. This tool is also a method for you to regain control of yourself. So, it needs time for your brain to latch on to the exercises naturally when you feel stressed again. At least you'll be prepared when anxiety strikes.

The Flurry of Options

Grounding has more options than most anxiety management tools. The choice you make will also depend on your situation when you use it. For example, you can't take a walk when you're in the middle of a meeting. However, there are methods you can use even in the most inconvenient places. These will be split into physical, mental, and emotional grounding to make your choices easier when you need them.

5-4-3-2-1 Method

This is the most commonly used method by therapists when someone's entering the shocked stage. Some people call this the five senses exercise because you need to see five things, hear four things, touch three things, smell two things, and taste one thing. Use this method the next time you feel a flood of emotions remove you from your current environment. Remember that you can practice it while you're calm as well to make sure you know exactly what to do when panic sets in. Let's see how it works.

You feel your heart racing or fear crawling into your mind. This is when you start recognizing five objects you can see. It can be anything, such as a tree, pen, paper, person, or a spot on the wall. Focus on naming five objects you see out loud. Use your inner voice if you're in public.

Next, recognize four sounds. I could maybe hear an airplane in the sky outside, music coming from my car radio, or a whisper of wind. Name four sounds you hear before moving ahead.

Now, focus on finding three objects you can touch. You can even touch yourself by stroking your fingers across your skin. You could also pick the pen up and feel it between your fingers. Touch the wooden desk in front of you. Touch and sight are the easiest to accomplish. You simply need to focus on each item and name it out loud.

Next, you must name two smells. Your sense of smell will be harder to reconnect with. Can you smell anything in the air outside? Maybe you can lower your nose and smell your perfume. You can smell soap in a bathroom or nature when you're in a park. You can also smell the leather of your car seats while you're driving.

Finally, name one thing you can taste. This is the hardest of the senses unless you have something you can place in your mouth. Make sure it's flavorsome, like something minty, or spicy.

Using your five senses in this manner will bring you back. There's only one warning with this method. Don't allow yourself to become too distracted by each item. You can also overdo the sensory stimulation and end up being further away from the present again. Stick to naming each sensory input and then move on to the next one. You can also swap the taste and smell steps around. Some people use taste and smell as the fourth step combined and then focus on a deep breath in and out as the final step.

Physical Grounding

This is a great option if you find yourself physically frozen. It helps to dedicate yourself to simple movements that help you cope better with a distressing thought rushing through your mind. Physical grounding can also peak your concentration if you find yourself in a situation where remaining frozen is more of a threat to you. Remember that the brain is trying to protect you from a threat and you can recenter yourself if you show it that the danger doesn't really exist. Keep in mind that you must focus on every movement you choose and each object you touch. Be highly descriptive about the texture, flavor, or temperature of each item.

One method of grounding yourself physically is to stop everything you're doing. Sit or stand straight and touch objects around you while you're describing them. You can use your inner voice or you can say them out loud. Talk about everything you touch and give them colors, sensations, and temperatures.

Press your feet hard into the ground beneath you so that you can feel your location. Focus on how your feet connect to the ground below and move them back and forth. Feel how the sensations change as the tension dissipates slightly. Your feet are grinding against the carpet and this causes mild friction.

Put something with a strong taste in your mouth and savor it. Don't simply swallow the candy or dried fruit. Swirl it around in your mouth and let it stimulate your senses.

Run cold water over your hands or stick them into a basin. How does the water feel against your skin? Feel free to change the water temperature and allow each shift to create new feelings on your fingers, palms, and wrists. You can also hold a warmish cup of coffee to experience temperature changes on your skin.

Pick up nearby items to run them through your fingers. Notice whether it's soft, hard, heavy, light, warm, or cool. Kick it up a notch and try to determine the actual color of the object. Don't just call it a red pen. Is it crimson or burgundy?

Breathing exercises can also ground you if you keep it even and feel the air pass through your nostrils. Focus on how it feels when it tickles your nostrils and how your lungs feel when your diaphragm rises.

Get up and take a sensory walk if you can. Pay attention to your feet's movements as you stride forward and take a detour through your favorite park. Kick your shoes off if you can and feel the grass on your toes. Feel your feet sink into the sand if you're on a beach.

Count your steps as you move forward to increase your concentration.

Take a piece of ice and roll it around in your hand. How cold does it feel against your skin? Keep holding it until it melts and notice how the texture changes as it turns to water.

Carry an essential oil in your bag. Take it out and smell the aroma of your lavender or cinnamon-scented oil. Make sure it's a strong one that brings you calmness. Scented candles, coffee beans, and spices can also work.

Surprise your body with sudden movements. You can stretch your legs, jog, or even do some jumping jacks. Pay attention to your feet hitting the floor as you jog on the spot.

Listening to your immediate environment can also ground you physically. Can you hear a dog barking? Maybe there's traffic nearby. Listen to voices if people are talking to you. Do everything you can to focus on these sounds.

Do a quick body scan to see where tension is building in your body. Use the PMR exercises to not only relieve the tension but also to focus on the feelings inside of you.

There are endless possibilities for physical grounding. These should give you many ideas that can even be implemented into your 5-4-3-2-1 technique.

Mental Grounding

Reconnecting your mental self is best when you enter shock, panic, or can't overcome flashbacks that are taunting you. You'll find these focal points best to divert speeding thoughts and bring your mind back to your body. Remember to pay attention to each type of grounding.

Describe your surroundings out loud in detail. What and who do you see? Is the tree in your yard blooming right now? Use words to describe how you feel as you look at every object. For example, I see my daughter smiling at me. This makes me feel warm inside when I look into those deep blue eyes. Her nose looks just like mine.

Play a memory game by listing the animals you saw at the zoo the last time you took the kids. Try listing them alphabetically. You can also recall all the actors from your favorite movie or series. Why not take a photograph and study it for 10 seconds before trying to piece it back together with your eyes closed?

Mental grounding can also happen when you categorize things. Use easy categories, such as baseball teams, mammals, yogurt flavors, or cars. Spend two minutes listing all the items from each category. How many car brands do you know?

The next option isn't a favorite to everyone, but some people have a "math brain." You can use numbers or math to center yourself. Process some equations in your head for two minutes. It can be anything as simple as adding one and one, or you can push your mind a little further with algebra if that's your thing.

Reciting numbers can also work as you try to remember the first phone number you owned. What was your first street number? You can recite anything, including poems, quotes, and songs. Focus on the way your mouth moves as you sing your favorite song.

Laughter can also work to ground you mentally. Make yourself laugh by logging into YouTube and watching people fail at homemade stunts. There's an endless stream of those videos and you'll find one that tickles your funny bone.

You could also anchor your mind with a mantra or a common phrase. Talk to yourself in the mirror and introduce who you are, where you work, and what your hobbies are.

Another great tactic is to visualize something you enjoy doing. Close your eyes and focus on an imagined picture of baking a cake. Interact with the visualization and talk about what you're doing. For example, I'm icing the cake right now. I'll design a pretty flower on the edge to finalize it. Imagine the smell and taste of your creation too.

You can even describe a simple daily task. How do you drive your car? Do you put your seatbelt on before you start the engine? Describe the steps you take before driving.

Finally, imagine leaving the fearful feelings behind. Close your eyes and picture yourself filling a bucket with emotions that frighten you. They're tangible in your imagination and you can feel them against your skin. Some may be hot and others might be cold. Bundle them together and walk to the edge of an imagined waterfall. Tip the bucket over and watch them as they disintegrate into the rushing water. You can imagine yourself driving away from your emotions or even putting them into a box and smashing it with a baseball bat.

Mental grounding can be achieved through most thoughtful actions and descriptions that allow the mind to focus on something other than the fear you feel at the moment.

Soothing Groundwork

The final exercise can be used at times when you enter an emotional state that doesn't allow you to interact with your environment to ground yourself. A time will come where you just need to calm down and focusing on these grounding techniques can help you do that.

One of the fastest ways to prevent distress and negative thoughts from flooding your mind is to visualize someone's face who you love. This can be a friend or family member that makes you feel happy. Imagine the sound of their voice and how it's calming you down.

Another soothing method is to practice self-kindness, which comes hard to anxious people. Face a mirror and talk to yourself compassionately. Say anything that you need to hear.

"I know this is hard but you can do it."

"I know you're scared but you're a brave person."

Pets are also great sources of calmness. Sit with your pet and stroke them. Notice all the markings and feel its fur to remind yourself of why you adopted this amazing creature.

Another strategy to soothe yourself is to revisit the journey to Peru example. Allow your imagination to take you to your favorite place and focus on being calm in that memory for a few minutes. Allow your senses to integrate into the visualization and listen to your breathing.

You could also plan an activity to soothe a distressed mind. Invite a friend or go alone if you want to. Do something you love like visiting a museum, walking on a beach, or popping into the farmer's market on Saturday. Give yourself something to look forward to.

Why not touch the soft carpet on your floor or run a smooth stone through your fingers? Touch anything that brings you calmness. It can be your favorite shirt, blanket, or silk. Wrap a soft scarf around your neck while you focus on the sensations between the fabric and your skin.

Turn the radio up and sing along to your favorite song. It doesn't matter what you sound like. Allow the anxious energy to move out of your body by singing loudly. Let the music drive you and calm your speeding thoughts down.

Finally, list five things that make you grateful or happy. It can be tiny or it can be the person who you're grateful for being married to. Positive thoughts can push negative ones off track.

Now you know how you can use grounding to target any stress you feel. Even panic and PTSD stand no chance against you if you master the art of grounding yourself.

Chapter 8:

The Art of Mindful Anxiety

Management

Mindfulness is like taking all the other anxiety management tools and blending them into a powerful eraser of concerns, worries, and stress. It has been studied to confirm the efficiency of applying it to anxiety management and has been hailed as a great tool. You're about to learn how to use it, combine it with previous methods, and apply it for more than stress reduction. Welcome to the ancient practice that's taken the modern world by storm.

Mindfulness Explained

Often, our anxious thoughts spiral into concerns about tomorrow, or we ruminate on the past. Mindful living is the most powerful method of grounding yourself in the present moment to help you get through difficult times and avoid unnecessary pain. Mindfulness is an art that requires practice, but you'll never regret learning how to be in full control of your life once it comes naturally.

Unfortunately, for many people, it's easier to live in our minds, but they don't realize the value of living in the present moment. Instead, you should be determined to master the skill of mindful living. It will bring so many benefits to your life.

You'll start enjoying the world around you because you'll be presently available to it. That includes all the people you care about and those who care about you. Your awareness grows and this allows you to partake in the joy of everything. You can't enjoy something your friends tell you about, but you can reminisce once you've experienced it. Your thoughts become positive because you'll start noticing all the little things you missed before. Positive thoughts will replace negative defeats. Your health improves as you live positively, including a drop in blood pressure, heart rate, and reduced stress or anxiety.

Mindfulness teaches you how to become reflective instead of remaining in the reactive state. The exercises show you how to become aware of the present environment while mastering the control you have over your mind. You won't be judgmental of yourself anymore. No sensations, feelings, or actions will make you feel bad again because you don't live in the past. Mindfulness practices help you distance yourself into a third-person perspective when you can't see things through first-person anymore. The past and the future won't be allowed to cause maladaptive thoughts or reactions again.

You learn to accept the person you are and all the strengths you have, and this is a powerful step forward in anxiety reduction. The Journal of Consulting and

Clinical Psychology published results from a behavioral-acceptance intervention which is part of being mindful (Roemer et al., 2008). Participants were suffering from GAD and were placed in an immediate intervention group or a control group. The intervention group had to train mindfully to accept who they were, what they survived, and the emotions they suffered from. A follow up at three and nine months showed significant changes to the intervention group. In fact, 78% of them didn't even meet the criteria for GAD anymore at the nine-month review.

These people weren't only able to erase the anxiety they felt, but they also learned to cope with stress in the following months. Their body awareness, focused attention, self-perception, and physical health improved. I'm sure you've noticed the key role that focus and attention play in your anxiety management. You can't be in the present if you're not paying attention to your immediate environment, body, emotions, and thoughts. Psychologist Ron Siegel also shares another secret with us (Siegel, 2015). We can retrain our brains to function in new ways with mindfulness.

The brain is remarkable with all the pathways that lead from one end to another. Those pathways are also known as habits, and our reactions to stress are nothing more than habits. Practicing mindfulness over time has shown to recreate the functions in the brain and lay down new pathways. Habits can only be formed by experiencing an event or response.

Rumination won't help you lay new pathways. Future concerns, whether maladaptive or not, also can't be experienced fully through your senses and can't redirect new connections in the brain. Teach your brain how to think, and thinking won't be a problem anymore. Teach it how to react, and responses will become realistically suited to proper prevention against genuine threats.

To make things even sunnier for you, mindfulness also teaches you how to bear anxiety in the future. Let's face it, anxiety isn't going anywhere in this lifetime. Life is filled with stress and triggers. We can't avoid anxiety altogether, but we can manage it and cope with the emotions that used to overwhelm us. The natural human instinct is to get rid of unpleasant feelings, but instinctive thinking takes the back seat to mindful thoughts. Emotions are present and you'll learn to accept them, but they don't drive your train anymore. You need resilience and mindfulness will give you just that. Fear and anxiety will become nothing more than words. Even fear has no power over you once you face it. It will simply dissipate as you learn to focus on it, much like giving a toddler attention so the tantrum comes to a halt.

How to Live Mindfully Every Day

At some point, you'll become like a Buddhist monk who can meditate for hours. But for now, you'll start implementing smaller and less stressful mindful practices into your day. There are some guidelines with mindfulness and you can apply each to your life as you become accustomed to the lifestyle.

The first thing you always remember is that you need an intention to make anything happen. Think of it as setting a goal. You must intentionally choose how you want your day to run. You can't lead a stress-free day if you don't choose to do it. Your intention gives your day structure and helps you to remember why you're doing this. My intention for the day could be as simple as not allowing my emotions to erupt.

Meditation is another option to lead a mindful life. It's best to start with guided meditations with apps like *Headspace* because it's hard to design your own at first. Listen to the guided session and allow yourself to immerse fully into it. Don't doubt and don't let your focus stray from the intention you set before entering one.

Doodling and coloring are also mindful practices because it allows your mind to redirect negative emotions into something beautiful. Get that app on your phone or buy a coloring book. There's no shame in adult artistry.

Walking through the park is also a mindful exercise. It grounds you and allows you to welcome all the sensations you hear, feel, see, smell, and taste. Don't walk without noticing every sensory input and allow them to control your emotions. I love the sound of birds and it's naturally calming to me.

Wishing other people happiness might not sound very fruitful, but it can create positive energy within you that resonates throughout your day. Try wishing five people a happy day in your mind. You don't need to tell them directly, and they can be strangers, colleagues, family, friends, or the supermarket cashier. Take it another step further by wishing happiness on someone who annoyed you recently.

Why don't you use your love of tea or coffee as a mindful practice? Become so immersed in tea or coffee-making that it brings you to the present moment. Talk yourself through making the cup, including everything you feel, hear, taste, smell, and see.

Learn to start looking up multiple times daily. Look at the beauty in the stars. Remove your eyes momentarily from the screen and watch nature in all its glory outside. Look for every bit of preciousness that exists around you. You wouldn't want to miss anything. Look at people when you talk to them and pay attention to the way their mouth moves. Think about all the things you could miss when you're not looking at what's in front of you. You'll miss the shooting stars while looking at the ground.

Multi-tasking is another anxiety creator that could be avoided through mindfulness. Commit to five minutes of partaking in any task before you move on to the next. This allows you to give undivided attention to what you're busy with.

Our phones can also distract us from leading a mindful life. Put it away and enjoy the present moment for what it is. Enjoy your family at dinner and listen to everything spoken. Don't allow your phone to deprive you of spending time with loved ones.

Bring your journal out and start recording everything you're grateful for and everything that upset you. You aren't ruminating on memories but only trying to deal with them head-on. Write your emotions down and let it vanish on the paper. Take its power away from your life.

Connect yourself to water so that you have something that's blending into your senses. Run water over your hands, shower, swim, or kick puddles with your feet. Feel every sensation as your body accepts the water as part of it. You can also drink water and feel the trickle down your throat.

Learn to savor your food instead of gobbling it down. Taste every bite and feel every burn of chili. Describe the taste and listen to the crunches as you bite into an apple. Feel the texture on your tongue and swirl it around your mouth.

Become intertwined with nature by standing at your window and describing what you see. Never allow the journey to be forgotten when you travel. Enjoy every step of the way and take in every scene with all your senses. Pull over when it's safe, and get out of your car to take a short stroll.

If all else fails, revert to the 5-4-3-2-1 method in Chapter Seven to ground yourself properly again. You should be using this method daily anyway. This is how you start living mindfully. It isn't a complicated instruction manual. You'll notice the changes in your daily life as you allow mindfulness to be your choice.

Learning to Dig Deeper

Meditation is the purest form of mindfulness and you can learn how to harness the power of it. There are some basic guidelines you can use while meditating. Some people prefer doing it at night because it brings about calmness before sleeping, and others prefer mornings when the mind is still freshly awakened from slower brain waves. Morning meditation also helps you prepare for the day ahead, reducing the anxious possibilities. You need four key reminders when meditating, whether you're using a guided session or learning to customize your own visualizations.

You must be comfortable, and the best is to position yourself on the floor with your spine straight while you cross your legs gently. The monks know how to enter the state of mind through physical positioning, but you're welcome to sit in the position that you find most comfortable. You can even lie down if you need to. The reason why people sit is so that they can be more aware of their bodies and to prevent themselves from falling asleep. There's no reason why you can't switch positions until you find your own comfort.

The second tip is to bring your awareness inward so that you connect to the present moment. Close your eyes and start with a breathing technique of your choice. You need to focus consciously on your breathing. It helps to pay attention to it without trying to change it at first. Once you become fully aware of it, then you can practice your technique. Bring your focus back to your breath whenever you realize your mind is wandering off.

Thirdly, don't judge yourself, your thoughts, or your emotions. Welcome them into your meditation and accept them. Mindfulness means that you need to accept the feelings inside of you. Don't try to erase the thoughts or emotions, but rather acknowledge and wait for them to pass slowly. Don't respond or react to them. It will take time to feel at ease with your thoughts.

Finally, end your meditation with reflection and gradual changes. Reflection is part of being aware of the changes in your body when you finish your meditation. Open your eyes and stretch your legs slowly. Welcome the calmer state and don't immediately jump up and start running.

These four tips will help you when you start designing a session of your own. Remember to keep practicing guided sessions because you'll pick up on the meditation that suits you. Everyone uses different types and you'll find comfort in the kind that helps you overcome your anxiety. Meditation isn't about suppressing your anxiety, but it's about overcoming it. You'll learn to cope with it, and it will help you deal with anxious thoughts that pop up during the day.

A final secret is to use an alarm clock that helps you keep track of time during your sessions. Trust me, it's easy to get carried away in meditation. I'll include a brief guided session for you, but remember to use an app like *Headspace* to learn how to meditate.

Weightlessness

I want you to find your most comfortable position and then you can listen to my voice. Don't allow my voice to consume your thoughts. It must only guide you as you enter a state of calmness. Listen to your breathing as you close your eyes. Can you feel the air passing into your diaphragm? How does the air feel? Continue listening to your breath as it slows down gradually.

The air goes in and it presses out gently. Once you notice the faintest pattern in your breath, you can count each inhale and exhale. How many seconds does each last? Are they becoming even now? Take your time. You can spend two minutes listening to the air moving through your diaphragm. Take five minutes if you need more time.

When you're ready, start counting your intake; one, two, three, and four. Hold the air in your body for a second before gently pressing it out of your mouth. Four seconds pass as the air tickles your throat when it exits the body. Do this for another five cycles. Count the inhale and exhale five more times. Your body feels a hint lighter with every exhale.

You want to release any tension you feel. You won't tense your muscles. You're only pushing the tension out mindfully. You're welcome to tighten a muscle that feels heavier than other areas before releasing it again. Notice how it feels when you pop the muscle loose. Scan your body to find any places that need some release. Either tense the muscle on your next inhale or focus on releasing the energy from it when you exhale again.

You want your body to become weightless. You'll take yourself to a place where your muscles weigh nothing. Keep breathing slowly, in and out, pressing every bit of air out that you take in. There's no force. It's a gentle blow outward as another tiny muscle releases the tension it holds. Give your body another scan from your toes up to your face. Are there any knots in your muscles?

Focus intently on releasing the knot while you push the air out of your lungs. Is the knot being stubborn? Try to tense it as you draw your next breath. Hold the air and notice how your muscle feels. Give the muscle permission to release the pressure inside of it. Slowly, gently, you continue scanning your body and removing tension as you reach the tip of your forehead.

Raise your eyebrows as you take a deeper breath now. Hold it until you've acknowledged and accepted the removal of the tension in your mind. Press your breath out a little harder now, but make it a long exhale to empty your lungs. Your entire body feels lighter; it feels weightless. Now, I want you to do something for yourself. Open your inner eyes to see where you are.

You're floating in space as weightless as anything would be without gravity. Keep breathing as you take in the essence of where you are for a minute. Just allow yourself to float about. You're currently in no pain. You have no anxiety right now. Your entire body and mind are floating through the cosmos, leaving you with a feeling you've never experienced before.

Take one more deep breath when you're ready and look beyond the empty vacuum of space. You can see the earth below. You can see all the anxious thoughts and emotions as hurricanes forming in the ocean. Don't look away. Face the unrest in the earth's water. Look at it and accept what you see. This is your world where your unpleasant thoughts and emotions are cycling in the oceans.

Keep your eyes focused as you recognize these watery problems. Don't let them overwhelm you. You accept that your world isn't perfect. No one's world is perfect. Continue watching these hurricanes as you notice them losing momentum. Never take your eyes off the thoughts and worries that cause your world to look scary.

The longer you look at them, the smaller they become. You can see one hurricane fizzling out like a flame dying in the wind. You see another hurricane dissipate before it reaches the shore. All the hurricanes are slowly disintegrating before your eyes. Pay attention to your feelings deep down now as you watch your fears vanish from your world.

You can stay as long as you like but come back to your world as soon as you're feeling calm, peaceful, and strong. You finally realize that the fearful hurricanes can vanish. They don't need to control you and any time they grow larger; you can revisit your cosmos to dissipate them again.

Focus on your breathing again as you count slowly in and out. Your inner vision grows more distant as you open your eyes where you're sitting comfortably on the soft ground. Your body starts gaining weight again as it reconnects to the ground beneath you. You never left the ground, but only gave your body the freedom to watch the hurricanes from a distant perspective.

Welcome the ground below again and allow your muscles to retain some weight now. Continue breathing for a moment as you reflect on the way your body feels now. You can't feel the anxiety that was present before you entered your visualization. You feel strong. You feel capable. You feel like you can do anything today.

I hope this session brings you some peace when you need it. Feel free to enter this cosmos as many times as you need to. Your imagination should take over once you reach your outer space visual. You can see anything in your world that your mind desires. Mastering your mindfulness will allow you to create the world you need to see.

Chapter 9:

Building a Strong

Foundation: Why Diet,

Exercise, and Sleep Matter

The tools you've collected so far are priceless in anxiety management, but you'll learn about the role played by your diet, exercise, and sleep now too. You need practical steps to improve every area of your life so that you can live without crushing anxiety now. Guess what? Even small changes can make a huge difference when you apply yourself to reducing stress and taking care of yourself. You've learned to retrain your brain, but now you must learn to improve your lifestyle and health from every corner because this will further abolish anxiety.

The Lifestyle Puzzle

Anxiety disorders are wrongly referred to as mental anguish, but too many people don't realize that it takes a toll on your entire body. Just as it affects your body, your lifestyle and choices can trigger worse anxiety. Let's look at every area of your lifestyle to make sure you can remove any unexpected triggers or manage them to reduce your anxiety in the long term.

Dietary Changes

You've brushed on the idea that consumables are harmful to your coping mechanisms, but dietary triggers can intensify something that seems so frightening already. Panic disorder and the physical symptoms of it can be worsened by the food and drinks you allow in your life (Star & Gans, 2020). Certain ingredients have proven to increase the frequency and magnitude of panic attacks.

Caffeine is one of the biggest culprits because we habitually wake up to a cup of coffee. However, it's confirmed to trigger panic attacks and anxiety. It also aggravates your irritability and nervousness. This daily trigger can also cause shaking and tremors. Let's not forget that it deprives you of sleep. What most people don't know is that caffeine is an addictive ingredient and abruptly removing it could lead to harmful withdrawal symptoms. It's a double-edged sword for anxiety sufferers. Alcohol and sugar have the same effect on you. They can aggravate anxiety further and disrupt your energy or sleep.

Monosodium glutamate (MSG) is another dangerous ingredient found in flavor-enhanced foods. It can cause nausea, dizziness, sweating, and panic attacks in anxious people. These ingredients all need to be removed from your trigger pantry slowly. Each one of them is addictive and you need to wean yourself gradually. The problem is that the gut and brain are intricately connected. One influences the other and vice versa. The brain's influence is so powerful that the mere thought of eating something can make the stomach release digestive juices.

However, the stomach is part of the endocrine system and any problems in the gut can signal the brain to trigger stress, erratically release hormones, and send your mental well-being down the drain (Harvard Health Publishing, 2019). This means that your stomach problems can be the cause or effect of stress and anxiety. Panic can cause the stomach muscles to contract, move, and create pain, but the gut plays a major role in the relationship with your brain and sends pain signals that cause you more distress. It's a two-way relationship that isn't good if you don't look after your stomach. That's why nutritional intake can trigger anxiety or worsen it.

You can implement a few changes in your life besides cutting back on the triggering ingredients. You need to remain hydrated and this means no more soda. You should be drinking water as though your sanity depends on it because let's face it, it does! Start making positive changes to your diet. You want to eat food that encourages good emotions and helps you raise yourself out of the plunder anxiety brings.

Begin with whole grains, vegetables, and fruit to counter all the bad carbohydrates that cause gut problems. Rather eat complex carbohydrates because the slow-release process helps your blood sugar remain normal. Avoid processed food and don't skip meals or your blood sugar will drop, sending panic to your brain. Add a few anxiety-fighting ingredients to your new diet instead.

Magnesium-rich foods such as legumes, leafy greens, nuts, and seeds are great options to include in your diet. Magnesium naturally calms you down.

Zinc is another anxiety-crusher and is found in egg yolks, cashew nuts, beef, liver, and oysters.

Omega-three fatty acids have proven to smash anxiety, in a study conducted on medical students (Naidoo, 2016). Medical students have tons of anxiety because learning to heal people isn't the easiest job in the world. If it works for them, it works for you. Omega-threes are found in fatty fish like salmon or nuts.

Probiotics are used to counter the negative effects of antibiotics because it replaces the good and necessary bacteria in your stomach. The good news is that you get foods with probiotics as well. Kefir, sauerkraut, pickles, and coddled yogurt are sources of natural probiotics.

Asparagus is one of the hardest things to cook perfectly, but it has many anti-anxiety benefits. It's always been known as a healthy option, but people tend to avoid it for the smell or toughness if it's prepared wrongly. Add some asparagus to your diet and find a recipe that works for you.

The vitamin B range has also been effective in the battle against anxiety. Foods most rich in vitamin B are avocado and almonds.

Antioxidants are another great source to maintain good gut health. Foods rich in antioxidants are beans, such as pinto, black, and kidney variations. You can also find it in vegetables like artichokes, spinach, broccoli, kale, and beets. Fruit containing antioxidants includes granny smith or red delicious apples, cherries, plums, and prunes. Blueberries, blackberries, strawberries, and cranberries also help. Walnuts and pecans also contain the ingredient. Spices and herbs can be useful too. Turmeric and ginger are the most famous antioxidant-containing spices.

Many of these stress-reducing ingredients also release serotonin and melatonin that regulate the sleep cycles which we'll focus on soon. The dietary changes also release a chemical called dopamine that soothes your mind as a natural calmative. Making dietary changes can be one more notch on your anxiety-management belt. Start small and allow the changes to snowball as you begin recognizing the benefits that come from it. Your diet doesn't only affect your anxiety, but it also creates a landslide into many areas of your lifestyle that could halt your progress.

Stress

Stress is another common trigger that we can't avoid. It's a normal part of life. You need to learn how to cope with daily stress by using the techniques you've learned about because it's been linked to anxiety over and over. Stress reduction can also be achieved through exercise. It improves your mood and raises your self-esteem and energy levels. Your body reacts better to stress when it's part of your lifestyle. You need to make a concerted effort to reduce your stressors in your daily life by using the combination of coping tools you've learned about. Stress can derail your progress and even though it's part of human life, it must be dealt with as best you can.

Exercise

Sedentary people suffer more easily from anxiety. It's not just our body-image and boredom that lead the way to higher risks for anxiety. It's also the movements of our bodies that can change the way we feel. Being physically active is another method for you to combat anxious thoughts, whether you're striking a punching bag with rage or you're using calming stretches to press the tension out of your muscles. Research has shown that aerobic exercise can alleviate the risk of anxiety and panic, while it improves sleep (ADAA, n.d.-a).

Exercise starts balancing the stress response in your body, keeping those chemicals in check. It also releases the feel-good chemicals that could bring your mood down when you feel overwhelmed. Dopamine is rushed into your body as a natural drug that brings you closer to reducing your anxiety. Some people have shown brief benefits from exercise, but other people maintain a healthier lifestyle which lessens the blow from stress. Aerobic exercise was proven to be the most effective when the ADAA suggested that emotionally drained people become more active. The beauty is that aerobic exercise can be achieved through simple routines. Join yoga practitioners, a tai chi class, or you can take a walk.

The research proved that a 10-minute walk is no less effective than a 45-minute workout. Your level of activity could be triggering anxiety and all you need to do is get out there and become active. You could make exercise even more efficient by adding a hint of nature to your routine. Sedentary people with anxiety are encouraged to exercise outdoors after another study proved that nature reduced our stress as well (Harvard Health Publishing, 2018b). Researchers focused on the connection between nature and our mood by using ecotherapy. The results have shown nothing less than reduced stress, anxiety, and depression.

The prefrontal cortex in the brain is linked to ruminating thoughts and it still lit up like the Milky Way when a control group had to walk in an urban setting. This was compared to a nature group, who walked through parks. The nature group showed reduced usage of the prefrontal cortex. The control group were suffering from prefrontal malfunction that's been confirmed to be active when anxiety sufferers can't overcome negative and debilitating thoughts or emotions. These people had high levels of stress which triggers anxiety. Instead, nature provides you with therapeutic cues that calm the mind down. Now you know why you see yoga groups in the park. How serious are you about defeating anxiety? If you're ready to change your outcome, you need to start now.

Exercise can also help you sleep better, which we're getting to soon. Begin with outdoor exercise, even if it's a slow walk in the park daily. Aim for 30 minutes every afternoon and remember to be mindful about your surrounding nature. You can run, jog, cycle, or take your dog for a walk daily. Stick with exercise that doesn't push your boundaries until you're ready to amp it up. Dancing is another option and it's a lot of fun to help you decrease bad moods. You can start by exercising five days weekly so that you have two days to recuperate from your routine. Frequency also matters more than intensity, so aim for spreading the workouts over the week.

Any form of exercise is better than none. Join a group session if you're not socially anxious. Meet new people and sign up at the gym. Getting involved in group exercise programs can motivate you and help you if you don't know how to strike a certain yoga pose. The most important rule of all is that you enjoy what you're doing and partaking in classes where people encourage you is one way of pursuing the fun side of exercise. However, it's okay to exercise solo if social activities are what makes you anxious. Allow yourself to come out of your shell before joining a group then. You can appoint an exercise buddy instead. Choose a close friend who can motivate you and make exercise fun. There are options for solo-ventures too.

Get yourself earphones and listen to uplifting music that creates a double-whammy anxiety-crusher while you exercise. Some gyms even have screens on the treadmills now so that you can watch something while you work out. Just remember that nature is the best place to exercise, but some days might not allow it. You aren't in control of the weather but you can adapt to indoor activities when it's snowing. Finally, don't be too hard on yourself if you've been sedentary. It takes people an average of six to eight weeks to get into a workout routine. Practice your breathing while you exercise and don't push yourself harder than you need to. Give it time and you'll see how exercise improves your health, emotional resilience, and sleep.

Sleep Hygiene

The final lifestyle change you need is to improve your sleep. You won't be winning over your anxiety if you're walking on your last ounce of energy. Sleep matters more than you know. Sleep and mental health are connected like conjoined twins (Harvard Health Publishing, 2018a). It's the final piece of the self-help puzzle for reducing your anxiety and leading a healthier, happier life. Sleep deprivation can push you over the edge, cause panic attacks, and disturb your psychological well-being. You'll struggle to manage stress and your emotions will take over. The emotional brain will be the driver if you can barely keep your eyes open.

Harvard Health explains that chronic sleep interferences affect between 50 and 80% of people with emotional disorders in America. It was originally thought that insomnia was merely a symptom of anxiety; however, it can also make you anxious even if you weren't before. Sleeping adequately has been shown to increase your emotional resilience, while insomnia causes an influx of negative thinking in the infamous prefrontal cortex again.

The science behind sleep has grown immensely. Everyone cycles through four major sleep patterns every 90 minutes, and they include deeper sleep where the muscles relax, and your temperature, blood pressure, and heart rate slow down. This is known as non-rapid eye movement (non-REM) sleep. The body is busy restoring itself and maintaining the balance in the brain.

The last cycle is called the rapid eye movement (REM) stage and this is where you dream. Our memories and thoughts can play like a movie in this cycle, but it's also where our long-term memories are consolidated and our capacity to learn is enhanced. The REM stage of sleep is also crucial to emotional stability as memories play a role in our capacity to deal with stress. Sleep disturbances cause the unbalanced and unnecessary release of hormones and chemicals into the brain that negatively impact your emotional resilience and thought patterns. People with OCD, PTSD, panic disorder, and phobias are more likely to suffer from sleep disorders and this worsens their anxiety. Insomnia can also prevent you from the freedom you need from stress.

Insomnia isn't only the inability to fall asleep. It also includes people who struggle to stay asleep and wake up frequently throughout the night. The good news is that insomnia is preventable with simple lifestyle changes. Relaxation techniques like PMR and meditation can help you fall asleep. Exercise can release the chemicals required to regulate your sleep, such as serotonin and melatonin.

Eating a healthy, balanced diet can also encourage better sleep, especially when you remove caffeine from your nighttime routine. Cognitive-behavioral therapy (CBT) has also proven effective in sleep regulation. You'll learn about this in Chapter 10. Breaking this double-sided habit that connects poor sleep to anxiety is also achieved through sleep hygiene.

Sleep hygiene isn't practiced by sleeping under a running shower. It's used to describe the act of cleaning up your sleeping habits. This includes your environment, bedtime routine, and lifestyle. You need to improve your sleep by creating an environment that's conducive to counting sheep. It starts with a schedule where you go to bed and wake up at the same time every day.

Your body has a clock that follows your habits. This clock also manages the sleep hormones. Make sure you give it a blueprint to work with. It might take time for it to learn new routines, but it *will* happen. Don't overwhelm your sleep routine changes either. Make small and gradual changes as habits can't be reformed overnight.

Start with pushing your bedtime forward by an hour. Don't change it from nine to seven on night one. Naps can also be harmful because they can interfere with your body clock. The human body only needs so much sleep and if you're napping away during the day, you're removing your nighttime sleep. Prioritize your sleep at night. Don't allow work, social events, or your favorite series to keep you awake. Your priority is to sleep as many hours as your new schedule allows. Remember that intention is a key part of mindfulness. Turn your schedule into a mindful one by making sleep the number one intention tonight.

Be consistent in your routine and develop a healthy bedtime ritual before you sleep. Maybe you could read a book or listen to a guided meditation. Control your environment by removing all electronics from your bedroom an hour before you go to bed. Dim the lights and control the temperature. Sleeping in a room that's too hot or cold isn't conducive either. Remove noises that keep you awake and invest in blackout curtains to prevent light from entering the room. Your bed must be comfortable and welcoming, and make sure your duvet/cover is sleep-friendly. Turn the environment into something that a baby will sleep in. Finally, give yourself a 30-minute window to practice the nighttime routine that makes you drowsy, even if you lie still in silence.

This chapter has focused on the lifestyle choices we can make to manage our anxiety better. Don't allow the idea of a lifestyle overhaul to make you anxious either. You're welcome to introduce changes in baby steps until you don't even notice them anymore. The habits in this chapter are all connected and you may even notice improvements in another area when you focus on a different one. For example, exercise automatically improves your sleep. Once you reach an overall lifestyle change that includes your diet, sleep, and exercise, you'll have a great foundation to manage your anxiety in the future.

Chapter 10:

Therapy and Medical Assistance: What are Your Options and When to Use Them

Following the self-help lifestyle and learning to manage your anxiety is often enough to get you back on track, but sometimes you might need some additional support. We weren't created to face the world on our own. Anxiety is a genuinely debilitating experience and you need to do me one favor before you proceed. Anyone who thinks anxiety isn't real or doesn't believe in getting the help some severely anxious people need should be shoved forcefully off the edge of the nearest cliff. Imagining this can already make you smile. If you feel that your anxiety isn't capable of being managed alone for the time being, please take advantage of the useful and temporary tactics laid out in this chapter.

An Ocean of Options

Are you feeling low or fearful even with all the amazing tools you have? That's fine because there are people who have studied psychology and can help you traverse the frightening waters of anxiety. Therapy is always an option and could work alongside your self-management tools. Only you know whether you need it or not. Well, there are so many options for you to choose to bring someone onto your anxiety battlefield. Increasing the numbers in your team is only going to enhance your ability and shorten the longevity of your journey.

I advise anyone who tries all the self-management methods and still watches anxiety alter their lives to speak to their family doctor about therapy. They might send you off to someone who can help or you can come prepared with basic knowledge of what you can expect. There are incredibly effective therapies that help you overcome anxiety.

CBT Collaboration

Cognitive-behavioral therapy is the first option you have. These therapists aim to find harmful thought patterns that prevent you from enjoying life. They focus on finding solutions to the foundation of anxiety and troublesome feelings. Even better, your therapist works with you and teaches you to continue using the CBT techniques that help you notice these maladaptive thoughts. Unpleasant thought patterns are called distorted cognitions in CBT. They can include catastrophizing, black and white thinking, or having a consistent sense of doom.

The therapist will help you uncover distortions and show you how to react towards triggers. You might have to face your fears and use simple exercises to find alternative thoughts because thoughts instigate behavior and emotions. Then, you can work on replacing them or coping with the stress surrounding the thought. CBT therapists are coaches, and they don't just sit there listening to you. Not that talk therapy is all bad, but these coaches are more proactive. Someone who suffers from black and white thinking will assume that every outcome will either be extremely good or bad.

The therapist will show them all the gray lines in between because anxiety prevents us from thinking rationally or realistically. The therapist will remain your coach for as long as it takes you to learn the coping strategies to use at home. CBT is the most widely-used and effective therapy for GAD, phobias, PTSD, SAD, and panic disorder (Cuncic & Morin, 2019).

Exposure Therapy

This is a subtype of CBT and is commonly used for PTSD, SAD, and phobias. The foundation of this therapy is that you must face your fears to overcome them. A therapist will slowly and gradually introduce you to situations or objects that make you anxious. This is known as systematic desensitization. The counselor will teach you relaxation techniques first before exposing you to anything. This includes PMR, breathing exercises, and meditation. They'll then ask you to list your fears in order of insanely intense to not so bad. Your triggers will be used to design your therapy.

The third step is when your therapist slowly starts exposing you to the mildest of your fears and works their way up as you become comfortable with the last one. There are also multiple methods in which your psychologist will expose you to these fears. They might use imaginative exposure much like visualization where you can overcome fears in your mind. In vivo exposure is probably the most frightening for anxious people because they have to face their fears in real life. For example, you might have to meet a new person at the gym this week if you're socially anxious.

The final exposure method is called virtual reality exposure and it combines the previous two into an easily manageable approach if in vivo isn't an option for you. This helps a lot for PTSD sufferers and can even help someone with agoraphobia by placing them in a virtual elevator. Exposure therapy is a great option and should be considered if you become increasingly anxious for reasons that you don't think should exist.

Acceptance and Commitment Therapy (ACT)

This form of therapy is gentler and works well for goal-orientated people. Your psychologist will help you define what your values in life are and set goals that remain within them. From that point, everything you do will align itself with your values. This form of therapy also considers mindfulness because you can't change who you are. You can only accept what you're capable of and commit to striving towards it.

Art Therapy

Art therapy works well because it allows you to mold into a creative experience instead of dealing wrongly with your feelings and thoughts. You don't even speak to the therapist if you don't want to. Instead, you express your emotions and thoughts by painting, drawing, or sculpting. Sometimes, expressing the pain can turn it into such a beautiful creation that it naturally helps us to process the anxious agony inside of us. Some of the world's greatest artists have dealt with immense pains in their lives. Frida Kahlo is a famous Mexican painter who expressed her pain through her work after she experienced a tragic incident as a child.

Her artwork doesn't only bring her fame, but it also allows her to separate herself from any thoughts and emotions that pile up inside of her. Creating an image of our anxiety allows us to diminish its power and pull ourselves away from it. I bet you that many of the greatest novels ever written are also soaked with experienced emotions from the writer, whether it was magnificently painful or a life-changing burst of happiness. Never underestimate the power of art. Art therapy and CBT also work well together.

Psychoanalytic Therapy

This kind of therapy is more traditional and requires real commitment and dedication from you. It originates from the father of psychotherapy, Sigmund Freud. Psychoanalytic therapists focus on finding the source of how you think about yourself. It looks for the deepest thought patterns, beliefs, fears, and desires to create a map of your brain. It's a great method of reducing anxiety once you understand why you view yourself as you do. The ultimate purpose of this therapy is to change the origins of negative or distorted thoughts and fears.

Interpersonal Therapy (IPT)

This is a choice for you if you struggle socially or have a bad history of relationships. A therapist will work alongside you to find solutions to your interactive problems in social settings. So, you guessed it. This type works well for social anxiety. However, you can also consider IPT for conflict with family and friends, unresolved grief, and coping with problems at work because you don't know how to interact with colleagues. You'll learn how to relate to other people and how to cope with sudden changes in the social setting. Moreover, you'll enhance your communication skills and find ways to express your emotions positively.

Other than the options here, your doctor might advise you on additional treatment options. Whatever you choose, all that matters is that you find someone who works for you. Don't be afraid to change therapies if you aren't comfortable with your first choice. You should give each one a valid try before moving on, but you'll know when it isn't working for you.

Making Therapy Work

Before giving up on any therapy option, I want you to commit to trying it. Therapy works best if you don't pretend to be okay when you aren't. Chances are that you're paying the therapist for their time and you want to get value for your money. Be open and never pretend to be fine if you feel anxious. Your therapist is trained to help you but they can't do this unless you allow them to. Ask questions to make yourself comfortable as well if you're feeling uneasy. Ask them anything because they'll answer you unless you're asking them to come over for dinner. Your relationship with them must just be professional, but you can ask for advice, tell them anything, and ask whether they think you need help.

Be honest about everything you need to talk about. It doesn't help if you're being dishonest because you're only wasting your money and the treatment won't work. Tell your therapist about your goals, and I mean all of them. Share the small ones that seem insignificant and tell them where you want to be in five years. They can even advise you about the expectations you hold over yourself. Heck, they might even help you recognize milestones when you reach them. It's easy to overlook the good when you're anxious. You should also share your healthier lifestyle choices with them because therapy won't work if you drop the anxiety tool belt you've collected on your way here.

Finally, build a social network even if you're socially anxious. A good friend can always fill the spot of a therapist between sessions when you have a meltdown. I'll emphasize it again. You were never created to face the world alone. The more people you have rooting for your team, the easier this journey becomes. Don't be shy about mentioning your therapy either because anyone who has anything negative to say about it can meet the cliff's edge we spoke about. Well, in your mind obviously. Surround yourself with positive, supportive, and encouraging people and watch yourself soar.

Medication

When all else has failed and life still feels like it's running you over; you can speak to your doctor about anxiety medication. Fortunately, there are so many available because everyone is unique. Not every kind will work for you and your doctor might try a few until one makes you manage life again. **Please keep in mind that the administration of anxiety medication should be managed and prescribed by a psychiatrist**. These medications affect the brain and the functions within it. They should never be used without the guidance of an expert. Let's see what they might prescribe for you.

Antidepressants

The first kind of medication they might suggest is antidepressants. This doesn't sound like it targets anxiety, but antidepressants are also used to manage anxious people. This type of medication targets the neurotransmitters in the brain, such as the communications and chemical releases that control your moods. It can take between four and six weeks before you notice a difference in your emotional state. There are three kinds of antidepressants you can use for anxiety.

The first is called selective serotonin reuptake inhibitors (SSRIs). This is usually found in Lexapro, Prozac, Citalopram, Celexa, Paxil, and Zoloft. This type of medication increases your levels of serotonin, which isn't only useful for improving your sleep. Serotonin also affects your sexual functions, appetite, mood, and memory. This drug can present some side effects too but most people can tolerate the medication without minor discomforts.

Side-effects can include nausea, dizziness, diarrhea, dry mouth, drowsiness, muscle weakness, and sexual function changes. The fact that medications come with potential side effects is the reason why you must discuss it with your doctor and try various kinds to see which one works best for you. Your doctor will start you on a lower dose and increase it slowly to see how your body and mind reacts to it.

The second antidepressant group is called tricyclics. These work similarly to SSRIs and your doctor will also gradually increase your dose over the first few weeks. Tricyclics work well for most anxiety disorders except OCD. Drugs containing this brain-altering combo are Anafranil and Tofranil. This one isn't often prescribed though because it's an older drug that has become infamous for some unpleasant side effects. Remember that you might not experience any side-effects, though.

However, some people suffer from blurred vision, dizziness, nausea, drowsiness, dry mouth, and a lack of energy. It can also cause constipation, vomiting, and weight gain. Yes, tricyclics are the infamous antidepressants that people complain about when they gain weight, but some people don't tolerate newer drugs and have to rely on these. Doctors normally switch tricyclics or lower the dose if there are adverse effects you don't like.

Monoamine oxidase inhibitors (MAOs) are the third antidepressant that works for anxiety. This drug is best used for social anxiety or panic disorders. Marplan, Nardil, Emsam, and Parnate are prescribed versions of MAOs. These drugs target specific neurotransmitters in the brain to increase them and allow feel-good chemicals or natural calmatives to be released. It's also an older drug that comes with possible side effects and restrictions. For example, you can't eat cheese or drink red wine while taking it.

It's also not advised to use this medication if you're using birth control pills, cold and allergy medications, pain relievers, and some herbal supplements. Using counteracting medications with MAOs can lead to higher blood pressure too. It can also lead to dangerously adverse side effects if you don't mention your current medications to your doctor. This drug works well for extreme panic, but it's up to you to talk to your doctor about any potential contraindications with your current medication.

Specific Anxiety Medication

There are three more medications that target anxiety and aren't double-classified as antidepressants. The reason why most doctors prefer to use antidepressants is that some sedative anxiety medications are highly addictive or their side-effects are unwanted (Healthline Editorial Team, 2014). Let's see what you can expect from each one.

Benzodiazepines are one of the most addictive choices as it's a sedative as well. It's commonly given to patients in shock over 72 hours. It's used for extreme anxiety and allows the chemicals in your brain to force muscle relaxation. You can calm down rather quickly, but this drug isn't always used long-term. Panic disorder, GAD, and SAD are easily treatable with benzodiazepines. Medications such as Xanax, Librium, Valium, Klonopin, Diazepam, and Ativan contain benzodiazepines. Due to the strength and side effects of this medication, it's often used for short-term treatments only.

Benzodiazepines can affect your balance, make you severely drowsy, and mess with your memory. Other side effects include confusion, headaches, depression, and vision problems. The addictive part of it is more dangerous for people who've taken it for longer than two weeks even with their doctor's advice. Never stop using it suddenly without your doctor slowly weaning you off of it because it can cause seizures or serious withdrawal symptoms. Only your doctor can regulate your usage, how long it must last, and how slowly you come off the drug.

Beta-blockers are also an option for anxious people even though it's a drug used for heart conditions. It's useful for treating social anxiety or symptoms of a panic attack. You might use it before attending a party or giving a speech because it reduces the intensity of your anxiety symptoms. It's a great choice for fluctuating anxiety where you don't need to take medication daily. It often comes in the form of Inderal and isn't addictive like the previous option. Most people have no side effects from this modern type, but some may experience dizziness, dry mouth, drowsiness, and fatigue. Even less common are side effects like sleep disruptions, nausea, and shortness of breath.

The final anxiety drug treatment is called Buspirone. This drug is found in Buspar and its generic forms. It can treat long-term and short-term anxiety, but it works slowly. It also targets the brain messengers and interferes with the chemicals to increase the feel-good release. It isn't as addictive as the benzodiazepines either, but it can take weeks to show improvements. Some side effects can include dizziness, nausea, and mild headaches. Some people complain about having unpleasant dreams or struggling to fall asleep.

The truth is that every drug you take has positive and negative effects if you don't tolerate them well. You might also not be listening to your doctor's instructions. Any drug that affects the brain must be managed consistently by a medical professional. Weaning off anti-anxiety medication must be medically supervised. Finally, never forget to mention all your current medications and conditions to your doctor before they hand you a prescription with strict instructions. Allow them to help you, but bring your side to the table too.

Make sure you continue your self-help exercises, healthier lifestyle choices, and mindfulness alongside your treatment from a therapist, medication, or both. The more tricks you have up your self-enhancement sleeves, the faster you'll reach your goals. Keeping all the self-help strategies going strong will help you step out of professional treatment and be capable of managing your anxiety alone when your therapist and medications are gone. You want to stay on track and you certainly don't want to pay a therapist for the next five years. Use your management tool belt to continue when treatment stops.

Chapter 11:

Looking to the Future:

How to Avoid a Relapse

Reducing anxiety is attainable, but the reality of relapsing into an emotional state is genuine too. It's crucial to keep healthy habits and use what you've learned going forwards once you get your anxiety under control and your life begins to feel like it belongs to you again. The possibility of relapsing will remain and you need to reduce the chances of this happening. You also need to learn what to do if it happens. You're missing the final tool to ensure a pleasant life from this day forward.

What Happened?

You finally learned to smile again and cope with stressful situations you frequently experience. Your life improved, you sleep better, and you've grown mindfully aware of all the great things about yourself. You've reached a goal and couldn't believe how it feels to obtain something you once thought impossible. Take this feeling and cherish it. You deserve the recognition and freedom that comes from reducing your anxiety and coping with life's attitude towards everyone. You've finally regained control over your future.

But wait, you realize that your sleep is changing again. You notice that you spend more time at home and have canceled plans with your friends for weeks. You're experiencing sweaty palms again and it feels like you have a knot in your throat when you try to speak to your boss. What has changed? You erased the minor stresses and learned how to cope with unavoidable problems. You're busy experiencing a relapse because let's face it, even the strongest lion falls when anxiety shoots its target.

Relapses occur because life is unpredictable. You're only human and your coping mechanisms can waver. You might even stop leading the life you used to diminish them and this causes you to become anxious again. You left your anxiety tool belt behind and treatments have stopped because you were doing so well. However, life doesn't stop throwing lemons at you just because you've learned to dodge them. Preventative and long-term care is needed for anyone who's experienced anxiety before.

You start by planning for this because we can't achieve anything if we don't prepare for the worst. I don't want you ruminating on past failures or to allow negative thoughts to consume you. Think of it this way. Being in control of your anxiety will allow you to lead a great life 90% of the time. There's always a chance that something bad happens to shake your ground. Having your plan of action is how you make sure it doesn't define your future. You remain in control by remembering how great freedom from anxiety feels and taking action to prevent relapses.

Prevention Plans

Whether you sought therapy and medication to help you through the worst of it, or you managed your anxiety with self-help techniques, you need a plan of action going forward now. Every self-help coping strategy and lifestyle change must remain intact to prevent problems, but your aftercare matters just as much. You start by understanding that triggers can be unpredictable. You might have your triggers worked out as you did in Chapter Three. Keep your triggers at hand for the preventative planning.

However, there are some triggers we can't prepare for. No one knows when life will end. You might lose a loved one and this will rock you even if it happened naturally and peacefully in their sleep. Divorce and separation are also triggers that we often can't plan for. Relationship problems come at their own time and not necessarily when we instigate them. Financial plunder could set you off track if you had to cover unexpected problems. You could even lose your job as the company starts retrenching people in this poor economy.

Conflict at work or between you and a friend could also spontaneously erupt. Anniversaries of life-changing events can make you feel overwhelmed even if you don't think so. You might have to suddenly move house and this is stressful. Minor stresses are also not always seen before they snowball. The subconscious mind is a powerful part of us. Maybe you passed an accident on the way home from work and saw something you weren't supposed to. Two weeks down the line, you find yourself in panic as your sleep is disturbed by negative images.

It isn't always the triggers that are most obvious either. You can't prevent a home invasion that creates new fears in your mind. You've developed a fear of walking alone after you were attacked. These are less-obvious triggers that you didn't prepare for when you first identified your anxiety cues. It doesn't mean that they'll impact your thoughts and behaviors any less. Relapse will happen if any trigger, new or old, sets off a momentous negative pattern in your thoughts.

Some triggers can't be avoided, but there are others you can identify as they come and work on methods to manage them. Hence, I'll advise you to repeat Chapter Three and the identification of your triggers frequently to pick the new ones up. However, planning ahead to prevent relapse will require you to have a change of mindset. Awareness is the first step you take in prevention. Knowing that life isn't a breeze every minute of every day is one attitude to adopt.

The second step is to identify the need for change. Ask yourself three questions whenever something new or familiar pops up and makes you feel uncomfortable.

1. What are the differences in the way I handle my finances, relationships, work culture, obstacles, fears, and trigger situations?
2. How would I implement these differential changes in future trigger situations?
3. How would I implement the changes in my everyday life?

Let's use an example here to help you understand how your mindset must change between triggers and regular situations. For example, my trigger is public speaking. However, I flourish in my relationships. So, the first answer would be that I'm confident and familiar with my friends. Familiarity is the key here because it helps me to be confident. So, when I compare this to my trigger situation of public speaking, I can find a way to implement a change in answer two. I'll increase my familiarity with public speaking by attending groups and classes.

The final answer isn't difficult either in this example. I can apply confidence in my everyday life by having an open-minded and curious attitude. The more I learn about any situation, the more confident I can approach it. This is how you use your regular life to prevent potential triggers in areas that make you anxious. Many people face anxiety in multiple areas of their lives, but they can always use the strength they have in another area to combat the fears in the trigger situation. I'm a master of finances but I get anxious at work. Use the same methods you do in your budgeting as you do at work to counter this trigger before it happens.

Before completing your prevention plan, you need to identify barriers that could stop you from using an alternative mindset to conquer fear. Ask yourself two questions before choosing your alternative reactions to trigger situations from examples in your life where you kill it.

1. Can I identify any behaviors or thoughts that prevent the current plan?
2. Are there any situations or people that stand in my preventative plan's way?

Don't allow self-sabotaging behaviors to lead to self-fulfilling prophecies. You've decided that the curiosity you have in regular situations is the answer to prevent triggers from upsetting you. What stands in the way of the curiosity you need? Often, your self-defeating thoughts are caused by past experiences and unbelievable expectations of yourself. Is the thought of failing to learn something new standing in your way? Why is this thought present? This leads to the second barrier. Maybe your teacher at school always called you stupid or your friends told you that you aren't intelligent enough to pursue a new skill by signing up for a course.

Listen to these suggestions because they map the truth of the barriers. These are other people's opinions and unless you know better, you shouldn't be listening to them. Any situation, person, negative thought, or self-defeating behavior is simply a smokescreen. It's an excuse your mind is trying to push into your thoughts. It's also possible for you to be the barrier. You might fear failure but you should approach this thought as you do any other fear. Rather say: "I will *only* fail if I set unrealistic expectations of myself." You're accepting facts because you can't decide to become a rocket scientist if your math abilities are below par. However, this needn't be a barrier if you simply remain realistic in your goals.

Avoid any people or situations that prevent your plan to change triggers into opportunities. The bottom line is that your prevention plan is made of two factors. Awareness of potential triggers is the first one you can't deny. The second one is a change of mindset you need to adopt so that you can use coping mechanisms from regular events to traverse the stress experienced by triggers.

Coming Back

Hope is not lost if you've relapsed from your anxiety management plan. You simply need to get back on the route to your goals. Never allow a stumble to derail you. Before anything, recognize that you've relapsed. Notice how your anxiety symptoms are returning. They could include sleeplessness, heart palpitations, feelings of unrest, avoidance, and changes in your mood or behavior. Don't let them get worse. Rather accept that you've slid back one notch. You might lack motivation, or withdraw from events you were enjoying. Avoidance is one of the first signs that something's wrong.

Do you avoid loved ones, frequented places, or tasks you were passionate about? Avoidance is the easy route, but you need to remember how awesome freedom feels and rather face your fears head-on as you did before. Your fears don't define you and every time you conquer one, it becomes easier to erase another. Commit to doing the opposite of what your anxiety is trying to make you do. Remember that there are psychological experts who can help you deal with serious phobias even if they're new. Speak to your doctor about therapy again because you can return to it. Your therapist doesn't expect you to be unbreakable after previous treatments.

You must ask for help. Never try to face anxiety on your own. Friends, family, and support groups are there for you. Remember the rules to make therapy or support work in Chapter 10. Be honest and open with the positively supportive person. Avoid the bad apples that tell you to get over it. Asking for help and returning to your preventative coping tools can help you get through it again. Use your journal to keep track of your anxiety and to express your emotions that are overflowing. Emotions need an outlet and you need to remind yourself of the great, mindful things you achieve every day.

Keep eating well and avoid anxiety-stimulants. Exercise and use the relaxation techniques that helped you before. Knowing that it helps already makes it work faster. Finally, dedicate yourself to cognitive restructuring by replacing all your negative thoughts with positive affirmations, similar to the prevention plan in the previous section.

Your sensitivity is at work because you think you're going to miss your deadline for a presentation. Counter this thought with another one from an area in your life that's bursting with strength. You could think about how you've never missed an appointment at your doctor's office. How did you do this? You called ahead and prevented it. You could use the same strategy to speak to your boss and ask for another day before handing over your work. Chances are that they'll allow this and the trigger event was avoided by having a positive attitude and using cognitive restructuring.

The most important rule after a relapse is that you return to everything that makes your world less frightening, even the temporary strategies. You did it once and you can always use the memory of how anxiety freedom feels to remind you why you need to do it again. Keep your life balanced because you can't cope with stress if you allow it to exist when it doesn't need to. You're all that matters, so start prioritizing your well-being.

Conclusion

Bianca Sparacino once said: "You've dug your soul out of the dark, you've fought to be here; don't go back to what buried you." To some, anxiety is a minor irritation, but to others, it's a debilitating condition. You don't need to worry anymore. You don't need to fear the symptoms anymore. The days of waking up with no energy and dragging your feet are long gone. Some people live in denial and think that anxiety doesn't exist. The statistics prove that either they're lying or they're lucky enough to not have experienced it yet.

The dark pit of anxiety carries too many descriptions. One person receives a call that changes their life drastically. They experience the most extreme version of anxiety when they can't breathe. They start sweating and can hear their heart beating to the sounds of trance or party music. It isn't unusual for someone to faint when the dizziness takes over. It also isn't unexpected when someone throws up. Fear is a dangerous master if you don't control it. Even subtle anxiety must be managed to prevent a life you don't want.

I have a friend who thought she was unbreakable. She took on mountains and defeated giants every day. The problem was that she did it the wrong way. 'Amy' was a woman in her prime of life. She was starting a new career in public relations and was married by 30. Her life looked like a goal many of us would want in our lives. She had no financial concerns, and her marriage was blooming. She wanted to become a mother by 35 and spread her wings to open her own company by age 40.

These dreams were realistic, and I was rooting for her. Unfortunately, it started to crumble when she learned that she couldn't conceive without medical assistance. She looked at her finances and voilà, she could manage her dream of becoming a mother. Anyone who has been through artificial implantation treatment will understand the stress of having doctors poke and prod you as you keep testing negative. Amy was a strong woman and she never gave up.

She started pushing herself harder at work to earn more and cover the ever-increasing costs of her treatments. This is where I saw some cracks in the story already because she was depleting her energy without replacing it. She was always striving for more, and her marriage began to suffer. Her husband needed her and experienced an accident that would further alter their lives. Amy couldn't see what was happening at present and started living in the future alone.

She would reach her goals no matter what it cost. By the time she was 34, treatments failed, her finances looked bleak, and her husband divorced her. She thought the divorce was spontaneous, but all of her friends saw it coming. It was after I became the master of my life that she called me. I could barely understand her through the tears. Fortunately, my experienced ears heard something far more sinister happening when she stopped talking.

Amy was struggling to breathe and I immediately contacted emergency services. Today, Amy is one of my team members who has learned to manage her anxiety, big and small. She learned a valuable lesson that day. Avoidance and denial don't help you. Resilience only exists when you have the tools needed to face these giants. She's happy and living a fulfilling life today, but it wasn't easy for her to admit that she needed help to manage her anxiety.

That's why I've shared all my knowledge and passion for finding the right solutions with you. I already had my anxiety under control but listening to the pain in her voice that night undeniably made me gather every tool I had to overcome my spontaneous pain and her ongoing anxiety. You need to understand every type of anxiety there is. You must learn how to recognize the cause and triggers of your anxiety because it won't look the same as mine or Amy's.

Make a promise to yourself that you can do this because I know you can. Missing opportunities in life isn't the only potential consequence because it can resonate throughout your physical and psychological health. Only you can stop it. Don't allow the thought of consequences to rattle your cage either. You have every tool under the sun to combat it. You are the person who'll defeat an insurmountable beast. I've only given you the weapons to do it.

Whatever you want your life to look like is merely a few steps away. Use the methods you've learned about to design a plan of action that suits you. You know what makes you tick and you're the person who can control your life. You have proper breathing exercises, mindful techniques, and groundwork that won't allow stress and anxiety to derail you again. Best of all is that you can pick yourself up after derailment anyway.

Nothing stands between you and the life you deserve. You have a vast myriad of self-help and expert options to manage your anxiety. Your doctor, friends, family, and the medical advancements made today can help you step forward. Your life and lifestyle will change as you want it to. Do you want to be successful? Do you want to crush stress like the measly bug it represents?

Dedicate yourself to your tools to make sure this happens. Remember that all the methods are backed by science. They've all been tried and tested. All you have to do is find the management tools that work best for you. No rule says you can't use all of them either. The more you manage your anxiety, the smaller the giant shrinks.

My final word to you is that you allow yourself to morph from the kitten to the lion.

References

ADAA. (n.d.-a). *Exercise for stress and anxiety*. ADAA.
https://adaa.org/living-with-anxiety/managing-
anxiety/exercise-stress-and-
anxiety#:~:text=Scientists%20have%20found%
20that%20regular

ADAA. (n.d.-b). *Facts & statistics*. Adaa.Org.
https://adaa.org/about-adaa/press-room/facts-
statistics#:~:text=Anxiety%20disorders%20are
%20the%20most

Alyssa. (2019, November 25). *The short and long-term
effects of anxiety on the body*. Mental Health
Program at Banyan Boca.
https://www.banyanmentalhealth.com/2019/1
1/25/short-and-long-term-effects-of-anxiety-
on-the-body/

Ankrom, S., & Morin, A. (2019). *How to breathe properly
for relieving your anxiety*. Verywell Mind.
https://www.verywellmind.com/abdominal-
breathing-2584115

Anxiety 101. (n.d.-c). *Anxiety 101*.
Medicine.Umich.Edu.
https://medicine.umich.edu/sites/default/files
/content/downloads/Anxiety-101.pdf

Anxiety Canada. (n.d.-d). *How to do progressive muscle relaxation.* Anxiety Canada. https://www.anxietycanada.com/articles/how-to-do-progressive-muscle-relaxation/

Benke, D., Barberis, A., Kopp, S., Altmann, K.-H., Schubiger, M., Vogt, K. E., Rudolph, U., & Möhler, H. (2009). GABA A receptors as in vivo substrate for the anxiolytic action of valerenic acid, a major constituent of valerian root extracts. *Neuropharmacology*, 56(1), 174–181. https://doi.org/10.1016/j.neuropharm.2008.06.013

Burke, D. (2012, July 5). *Panic disorder.* Healthline. https://www.healthline.com/health/panic-disorder

Chirney, K., & Legg, T. J. (2014, September 24). *12 effects of anxiety on the body.* Healthline. https://www.healthline.com/health/anxiety/effects-on-body#The-effects-of-anxiety-on-the-body

Cirino, E. (2017, October 20). *Health anxiety (hypochondria).* Healthline. https://www.healthline.com/health/health-anxiety

Counselling Directory UK. (2013a, November 8). *Anxiety and relapse prevention (part 1).* Counselling Directory UK. https://www.counselling-directory.org.uk/memberarticles/anxiety-and-relapse-prevention-part-1

Counselling Directory UK. (2013b, November 14). *Anxiety and relapse prevention (part 2).* Counselling Directory UK. https://www.counselling-directory.org.uk/memberarticles/anxiety-and-relapse-prevention-part-2

Cuncic, A., & Morin, A. (2019). *The best types of anxiety therapy.* Verywell Mind. https://www.verywellmind.com/anxiety-therapy-4692759

Davies, M. N., Verdi, S., Burri, A., Trzaskowski, M., Lee, M., Hettema, J. M., Jansen, R., Boomsma, D. I., & Spector, T. D. (2015). Generalised anxiety disorder – A twin study of genetic architecture, genome-wide association and differential gene expression. *PLOS ONE*, 10(8), e0134865. https://doi.org/10.1371/journal.pone.0134865

Deering, S. (2020, February 28). *8 grounding techniques for when you're feeling overwhelmed.* Talkspace. https://www.talkspace.com/blog/grounding-techniques-anxiety/

Donohue, M. (2012). *Post-traumatic stress disorder (PTSD).* Healthline. https://www.healthline.com/health/post-traumatic-stress-disorder

Felman, A., & Browne, D. (2020, January 11). *Anxiety: Overview, symptoms, causes, and treatments.* Medical News Today. https://www.medicalnewstoday.com/articles/323454#causes

Ferreira, M. (2020, February 11). *Mindfulness tricks to help reduce anxiety*. Healthline. https://www.healthline.com/health/mindfulness-tricks-to-reduce-anxiety#1

Finglas, P. (n.d.). *Trends in Food Science & Technology*. Trends in Food Science & Technology. https://www.journals.elsevier.com/trends-in-food-science-and-technology

Gotter, A., & Legg, T. J. (2019, April 22). *8 breathing exercises for anxiety you can try right now*. Healthline. https://www.healthline.com/health/breathing-exercises-for-anxiety#equal-breath

Hall, C. B., & Lundh, L.-G. (2018). Brief therapist-guided exposure treatment of panic attacks: A pilot study. *Behavior Modification*, 43(4), 564–586. https://doi.org/10.1177/0145445518776472

Harvard Health Publishing. (2010, May). *Pain, anxiety, and depression*. Harvard Health. https://www.health.harvard.edu/mind-and-mood/pain-anxiety-and-depression

Harvard Health Publishing. (2018a, June 19). *Sleep and mental health*. Harvard Health; Harvard Health. https://www.health.harvard.edu/newsletter_article/sleep-and-mental-health

Harvard Health Publishing. (2018b, July). *Sour mood getting you down? Get back to nature*. Harvard Health. https://www.health.harvard.edu/mind-and-mood/sour-mood-getting-you-down-get-back-to-nature

Harvard Health Publishing. (2019). *The gut-brain connection*. Harvard Health; Harvard Health. https://www.health.harvard.edu/diseases-and-conditions/the-gut-brain-connection

Headspace. (2018). *How to reduce anxiety*. Headspace. https://www.headspace.com/articles/how-to-reduce-anxiety

Headspace. (2019a). *Meditation for anxiety*. Headspace. https://www.headspace.com/meditation/anxiety

Healthline Editorial Team. (2014). *List of anxiety drugs*. Healthline. https://www.healthline.com/health/anxiety-drugs

Healthline Editorial Team, & Legg, T. J. (2014, August 18). *Anxiety causes*. Healthline. https://www.healthline.com/health/anxiety-causes#risk-factors

Higuera, V. (2012, July 2). *Social anxiety disorder*. Healthline. https://www.healthline.com/health/anxiety/social-phobia

Hofmann, S. G., Sawyer, A. T., Witt, A. A., & Oh, D. (2010). The effect of mindfulness-based therapy on anxiety and depression: A meta-analytic review. *Journal of Consulting and Clinical Psychology*, 78(2), 169–183. https://doi.org/10.1037/a0018555

Hoggard, E. (2017, September 19). *Recognise your fight or flight (or freeze) responses.* Happiful Magazine. https://happiful.com/recognise-your-fight-or-flight-or-freeze-responses/

Holland, K. (2018, September 19). *Everything you need to know about anxiety.* Healthline. https://www.healthline.com/health/anxiety#symptoms

Holland, K., & Legg, T. J. (2018, May 1). *11 anxiety triggers and how to identify and manage them.* Healthline. https://www.healthline.com/health/anxiety/anxiety-triggers#1

International Bipolar Foundation. (n.d.-e). *18 ways to distract from anxiety.* International Bipolar Foundation. https://ibpf.org/articles/18-ways-to-distract-from-anxiety/

Johnson, S. (2017, November 8). *Separation anxiety disorder.* Healthline. https://www.healthline.com/health/anxiety/separation-anxiety

Kind, S. (2014, November 10). *Can mindfulness really help reduce anxiety?* Anxiety.Org. https://www.anxiety.org/can-mindfulness-help-reduce-anxiety

Klamer, H. (2018, December 12). *The 7 best drinks to reduce your anxiety.* Anxiety, Panic & Health. https://anxietypanichealth.com/2018/12/11/the-7-best-drinks-to-reduce-your-anxiety/

Lara, D. R. (2010). Caffeine, mental health, and psychiatric disorders. *Journal of Alzheimer's Disease : JAD*, 20 Suppl 1, S239-48. https://doi.org/10.3233/JAD-2010-1378

Leonard, J., & Legg, T. J. (2018, July 18). *Symptoms, signs, and side effects of anxiety.* Medical News Today. https://www.medicalnewstoday.com/articles/3 22510#causes

Linder, J. N. (2020, February 8). *Mindfulness and anxiety.* Psychology Today. https://www.psychologytoday.com/gb/blog/m indfulness-insights/202002/mindfulness-and-anxiety

Naidoo, U. (2016, April 13). *Nutritional strategies to ease anxiety.* Harvard Health Blog. https://www.health.harvard.edu/blog/nutrition al-strategies-to-ease-anxiety-201604139441

Nunez, K., & Legg, T. J. (2020, February 21). *Fight, flight, or freeze: How we respond to threats.* Healthline. https://www.healthline.com/health/mental-health/fight-flight-freeze#in-the-body

Owens, B. (n.d.). *How to recognize and overcome triggers for anxiety.* Talbott Campus. https://talbottcampus.com/how-to-recognize-and-overcome-triggers-for-anxiety/

Pathways Psychology Services. (2019b, April 16). *Long term effects of stress and anxiety.* Pathways Psychology Services. https://pathways-psychology.com/long-term-effects-of-stress-and-anxiety/

Raypole, C. (2019, May 24). *30 grounding techniques to quiet distressing thoughts.* Healthline. https://www.healthline.com/health/grounding-techniques

Robinson, D. (2015). *OCD: Symptoms, signs & risk factors.* Healthline. https://www.healthline.com/health/ocd/social-signs

Robinson, O. J., Vytal, K., Cornwell, B. R., & Grillon, C. (2013). The impact of anxiety upon cognition: Perspectives from human threat of shock studies. *Frontiers in Human Neuroscience,* 7(203). https://doi.org/10.3389/fnhum.2013.00203

Roemer, L., Orsillo, S. M., & Salters-Pedneault, K. (2008). Efficacy of an acceptance-based behavior therapy for generalized anxiety disorder: Evaluation in a randomized controlled trial. *Journal of Consulting and Clinical Psychology,* 76(6), 1083–1089. https://doi.org/10.1037/a0012720

Siegal, R. (2015, August 28). *A simple mindfulness practice that can lower anxiety.* NICABM. https://www.nicabm.com/mindfulness-how-mindfulness-can-help-your-clients-manage-anxiety-a-short-practice-for-befriending-fear/

Smith, S. (2018, April 10). *5-4-3-2-1 coping technique for anxiety*. Rochester Education. https://www.urmc.rochester.edu/behavioral-health-partners/bhp-blog/april-2018/5-4-3-2-1-coping-technique-for-anxiety.aspx

Star, K. (2020, September 17). *How to distract yourself from panic disorder*. Verywell Mind. https://www.verywellmind.com/distraction-techniques-for-panic-disorder-2584138

Star, K., & Gans, S. (2018). *Mindfulness meditation exercise for anxiety*. Verywell Mind. https://www.verywellmind.com/mindfulness-meditation-exercise-for-anxiety-2584081

Star, K., & Gans, S. (2019). *A step-by-step guide to using progressive muscle relaxation (PMR)*. Verywell Mind. https://www.verywellmind.com/progressive-muscle-relaxation-pmr-2584097

Star, K., & Gans, S. (2020, April 22). *Using a healthy diet and exercise in your life for reducing anxiety*. Verywell Mind. https://www.verywellmind.com/diet-exercise-and-anxiety-2584062

Star, K., & Ludwig, E. (2019). *Visualization techniques can help manage your symptoms*. Verywell Mind. https://www.verywellmind.com/visualization-for-relaxation-2584112

Suni, E., & Vias, N. (2019). *What is sleep hygiene?* National Sleep Foundation. https://www.sleepfoundation.org/articles/sleep-hygiene

Supreme Movement. (n.d.-f). *Breathing exercises &
benefits.* Supreme Movement.
https://www.suprememovement.co.uk/breathi
ng-exercises

Supreme Movement. (n.d.-g). *Distraction techniques |
mental health exercises.* Supreme Movement.
https://www.suprememovement.co.uk/self-
harm-self-help

Supreme Movement. (n.d.-h). *Grounding techniques.*
Supreme Movement.
https://www.suprememovement.co.uk/groundi
ng-techniques

Supreme Movement. (n.d.-i). *Mindfulness exercises &
benefits.* Supreme Movement.
https://www.suprememovement.co.uk/mindfu
lness

Supreme Movement. (n.d.-j). *Progressive muscle relaxation
exercises.* Supreme Movement.
https://www.suprememovement.co.uk/muscle-
relaxation

The Recovery Village, Hull, M., & Crowly, C. (2019,
September 11). *Anxiety triggers.* The Recovery
Village.
https://www.therecoveryvillage.com/mental-
health/anxiety/related/anxiety-triggers/

Weingus, L. (2015, June 24). *7 celebrities describe what it's
like to suffer a panic attack.* HuffPost Canada.
https://www.huffpost.com/entry/celebrities-
anxiety-panic-attacks_n_7639478

Wodele, A. (2011, December 31). *Phobias: Causes, types, and symptoms.* Healthline. https://www.healthline.com/health/phobia-simple-specific

Made in the USA
Middletown, DE
22 December 2020

29963034R00095